First Star
The Blue-Pillowed Sky
A Shiny Golden Path
Rainbow Bridge
Slide Down the Sky
From Sea to Shining Sea
Time for Dreams
Across the World
Over the Moon
Sound of the Sea
Promises to Keep

A little road was straying
   Across a little hill.
I asked, "May I go with you, Road?"
   It answered, "If you will."

'Twas travel-stained and shabby,
   And dust was on its face.
Said I: "How fine to wander free
   To every lovely place!
"O, if you're off to mountains
   Or if you're off to sea,
Or if you're bound across the world,
   It's all the same to me."

We loitered in the sunlight,
   We journeyed on together;
The sky was like a bluebird's wing,
   The wind was a like a feather.

                    —Nancy Byrd Turner

# Across the World

An anthology
compiled and edited by

**Zena Sutherland** and **Marilyn F. Cunningham**

**Program Authors**

Carl Bereiter
Marlene Scardamalia
Ann Brown
Valerie Anderson
Joseph Campione
Walter Kintsch

Open Court
La Salle, Illinois

**President and Publisher**
M. Blouke Carus

**Education Director**
Carl Bereiter

**Project Coordination**
Marsha Roit

**Project Planning and Implementation**
Thomas G. Anderson,
Commonwealth Strategies, Inc.

**Senior Editor**
Marilyn F. Cunningham

**Permissions**
Diane Sikora

**Art Direction**
Todd Sanders

**Cover Design**
James Buddenbaum

# Acknowledgments

Grateful acknowledgment is given to the following publishers and copyright owners for permission granted to reprint selections from their publications. All possible care has been taken to trace ownership and secure permission for each selection included.

Atheneum Publishers, Inc., a division of Macmillan, Inc.: for *Jonah and the Great Fish*, retold and illustrated by Warwick Hutton (a Margaret K. McElderry Book), copyright © 1984 by Warwick Hutton; for an adaptation from *To Sail a Ship of Treasures* by Lisl Weil, text and pictures copyright © 1984 by Lisl Weil, and for "Until I Saw the Sea," from *I Feel the Same Way* by Lilian Moore, copyright © 1967 by Lilian Moore.

The Estate of John Ciardi, for "Sizes," from *The Man Who Sang the Sillies* by John Ciardi; copyright © 1961 by John Ciardi.

Delacorte Press/Seymour Lawrence and William Jay Smith, for "Polar Bear," excerpted from *Laughing Time: Nonsense Poems* by William Jay Smith, published by Delacorte Press, 1980; copyright © 1953, 1955, 1956, 1957, 1959, 1968, 1969, 1974, 1977, 1980 by William Jay Smith.

Doubleday & Company, Inc., for "Who?" from *Moon-Uncle, Moon-Uncle*, selected and translated by Sylvia Cassedy and Parvathi Thampi; copyright © 1973 by Sylvia Cassedy and Parvathi Thampi.

E. P. Dutton, a division of New American Library, and David Higham Associates, Ltd., for "Tortoise and Elephant," adapted from *Tortoise Tales* by Ruth Manning-Sanders; copyright © 1972, 1974 by Ruth Manning-Sanders.

Eleanor Farjeon, for "Cats," from *The Children's Bells* by Eleanor Farjeon; © 1960 by Eleanor Farjeon.

Harcourt Brace Jovanovich, Inc., for the poem on page ii, from "The Little Road," in *Magpie Lane* by Nancy Byrd Turner; copyright 1927 by Harcourt Brace Jovanovich, Inc., renewed 1955 by Nancy Byrd Turner.

Harper & Row, Publishers, Inc.: for "Again and Again" and "Please Bird," from *Flower, Moon, Snow: A Book of Haiku* by Kazue Mizumura (Thomas Y. Crowell), copyright © 1977 by Kazue Mizumura; and for adapted text from *Paul Gauguin* by Adeline Peter and Ernest Raboff, copyright © 1987 by LRN Company.

Margaret Hillert, for "Puddle Wonder" by Margaret Hillert, reprinted from the March 1974 issue of *Cricket* magazine; copyright © 1974 by Margaret Hillert.

Felice Holman, for "Who Am I?" from *At the Top of My Voice and Other Poems* by Felice Holman; text copyright © 1970 by Felice Holman.

# Illustration

Franz Altschuler (51, 52, 53, 54), Enrico Arno (37, 40), Corinne and Robert Borja (76, 77, 78, 79, 80, 133, 134), Ralph Creasman (118), Jim Cummins (103, 105), David Cunningham (161), Susan David (178), Kies deKieffte (152, 153, 155), Bert Dodson (55, 57, 60, 62, 64, 172, 173, 175, 177), Tom Dunnington (65, 66, 67), Lois Ehlert (101, 102), Leonard Fisher (137, 139, 140), Peggy Fortnum (12, 14, 17, 18), Gauguin (157, 159, 160), Ken Goldammer (cover), Kate Greenaway (42, 43, 44-45, 46), Lydia Halverson (83, 86-87, 88-89, 90-91, 92-93, 94-95, 96, 164), Jean Cassels Helmer (135), Warwick Hutton (69, 71, 72-73, 74), Trina Schart Hyman (27, 30, 34), Laurie Jordan (6), Christa Kieffer (68), Joanna Adamska Koperska (4-5, 9, 49, 99, 131, 170, 171), Barbara Lanza (143), Janet LaSalle (81), Ron Lehew (119), Blair Lent (123, 124, 125, 126, 127, 128), Diana Magnuson (162-163), Benton Mahan (19), Yoshi Miyake (192-193, 194-195), Eileen Neill (179), Anita Nelson (35), Ben Otero (197, 198, 200-201, 203, 204), Brian Pinkney (184, 186, 189, 191), Allen Say (144, 146, 149, 150, 151), Steve Schindler (120-121, 122), Arvis Stewart (196), George Suyeoka (136), Alan Tiegreen (205, 206, 207, 209), Lisl Weil (20, 21, 23, 24), Jan Wills (82, 85, 106, 108, 109, 112), Leslie Wolf (border 11-18).

# Photography

Baltimore Museum of Art (160), Lee Boltin Picture Library (79, 80), Harry Burton, Treasures of Tutankhamen Catalog (75, 77), Walter Chandoha (113, 115, 116), Field Museum of Natural History (165), Lyndon B. Johnson Space Agency (1), Kunstmuseum, Basel (159), Minneapolis Institute of Art (157), Photri (142), *Ranger Rick,* December 1985 (180, 181, 182).

# Contents

# Unit Two   The Mediterranean

# Unit Three   Africa

# Unit Four    Asia and the Pacific

# Unit Five    The Americas

# The World and Its People

The country we live in is called the United States of America. The United States is a very big country, and millions of people live here. But the world is much larger and has many other countries. Most of the people in the world live in these other countries.

People in most of these other countries do not speak the same language that we do or use the same kind of money. They may dress differently from the way we do. The food they eat and the houses they live in are sometimes very different from ours.

Thousands of years ago people did not know anything about faraway lands or the people who lived in those lands. People could not travel from one place to another so easily or so quickly as they can today. They could only walk, ride an animal, or sail in a boat, when they wanted to visit a faraway place. They could not read about different places and different people because there were no newspapers or books. Instead, people used to gather together and listen to a storyteller or a traveler tell stories about faraway places. Because people did not know what the rest of the world was like, they imagined what it *might* be like.

In some ways people have not changed very much since that time. We still like to hear about new places and people. But now it is much easier to learn about them. Today we can telephone almost anywhere in the world in a matter of seconds. We can see what is happening in distant countries on the television news. We can even fly almost anywhere on earth in less than a day. The world has not become any smaller, but it has grown much more familiar to us. Today we know more about other countries and their people than ever before.

In this book you will take an imaginary trip around the world to visit faraway lands. You will read some of the folk tales and fairy tales of these countries. You will learn something about the way people there live and think. Even though they live far away, speak different languages, wear different clothes, or eat different foods—they think about many of the same things that you do.

Perhaps after you have read this book the world will not seem like such a strange and unfamiliar place. You will see that we are all people together, in this world of ours, with thoughts to share—and stories to tell!

# COUNTRIES OF THE WORLD

| THE AMERICAS | 9 Haiti | 15 St. Vincent and | EUROPE | 28 Liechtenstein |
|---|---|---|---|---|
| | 10 Dominican | the Grenadines | | 29 Austria |
| 1 Guatemala | Republic | 16 Barbados | 20 Denmark | 30 Hungary |
| 2 Belize | 11 St. Christopher | 17 Netherlands | 21 Netherlands | 31 Andorra |
| 3 El Salvador | and Nevis | Antilles | 22 Belgium | 32 Monaco |
| 4 Honduras | 12 Antigua and | 18 Grenada | 23 Luxembourg | 33 San Marino |
| 5 Nicaragua | Barbuda | 19 Trinidad and | 24 West Germany | 34 Yugoslavia |
| 6 Costa Rica | 13 Dominica | Tobago | 25 East Germany | 35 Albania |
| 7 Panama | 14 St. Lucia | | 26 Czechoslovakia | 36 Malta |
| 8 Jamaica | | | 27 Switzerland | |

ARCTIC OCEAN

NORWAY
FINLAND
SWEDEN
SOVIET UNION
EUROPE
POLAND
MONGOLIA
ROMANIA
BULGARIA
ITALY
TURKEY
GREECE
SYRIA
IRAQ
IRAN
LIBYA
EGYPT
SAUDI
ARABIA
YEMEN
OMAN
ALGERIA
AFRICA
NIGER
CHAD
SUDAN
NIGERIA
CEN.
AFR. REP.
ETHIOPIA
GABON
CONGO
ZAIRE
TANZANIA
ANGOLA
ZAMBIA
NAMIBIA
MADAGASCAR
MAURITIUS
BOTSWANA
ZIMBABWE
MOZAMBIQUE
SOUTH AFRICA

ASIA
AFGHANISTAN
CHINA
PAKISTAN
INDIA
BURMA
THAILAND
VIETNAM
MALAYSIA
INDONESIA

N.KOREA
S.KOREA
JAPAN
TAIWAN
PHILIPPINES
PACIFIC OCEAN

P.D.R. OF
YEMEN
SOMALIA
MALDIVES
SRI
LANKA
KENYA
SEYCHELLES
COMOROS
INDIAN OCEAN

NAURU
PAPUA
NEW GUINEA
SOLOMON
ISLANDS
TUVALU
FIJI
VANUATU
AUSTRALIA
NEW ZEALAND

# Where Is a Poem?

EVE MERRIAM

Where is a poem?
As far away
As a rainbow span,
Ancient Cathay,
Or Afghanistan;

Or it can be near
As where you stand
This very day
On Main Street here
With a poem
In your hand.

# Unit One
## Northern Europe

# Northern Europe

The first stop on our imaginary trip around the world is the northern part of the continent of Europe. To get to Europe from the United States we have to cross the Atlantic Ocean. Five hundred years ago it took Christopher Columbus more than a month to sail across the Atlantic. Today, in a jet plane, the trip takes less than six hours.

Look at the map of northern Europe on page 9. The many countries are all different sizes. Tiny Luxembourg is smaller than the smallest state in the United States. The Soviet Union, which lies half in Europe and half in the continent of Asia, is the largest country in the world. Even though European countries are right next to each other, the peoples of Europe speak many different languages.

The weather is very mild in much of Europe. This helps the people grow many crops on their rich farmlands. Do you see how much of Europe is surrounded by water? For hundreds of years Europeans have sailed the seas to trade goods, to fish for food, and to explore new lands.

The fine weather, rich farmlands, and many seaports have helped Europeans become world leaders for over a thousand years. The stories you are about to read will give you an idea of how Europeans live and what they think.

Since long before the age of airplanes, most parts of the island of England have been connected by a huge system of

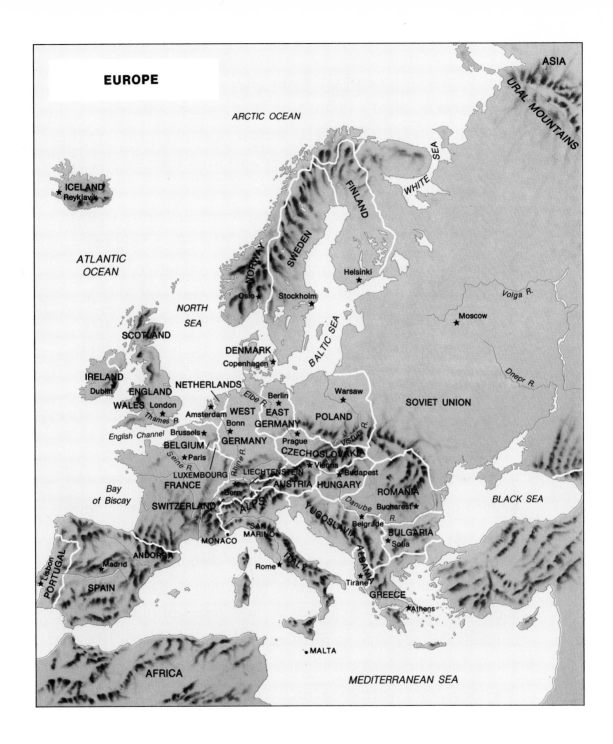

EUROPE

9

railroad tracks. One of the main railway stations in the city of London is called Paddington. That's where a bear is found in the play called "The Arrival of Paddington." In this play you'll see how the English people love animals, tea, and cakes—and a good joke!

Paddington Bear has cakes and marmalade in a train station in London. In the story called "To Sail a Ship of Treasures," a little girl named Lisl eats frankfurters and horseradish in a coffee house in Vienna, Austria. Lisl tells you all sorts of things about her life in this beautiful city. When she has to leave Vienna, she tells you how it is both sad and exciting to make a new home in a strange country.

People all over the world like to tell stories. Many of your favorite folk and fairy tales come from Europe. "Beauty and the Beast" comes from France. It has an enchanted castle, a handsome prince, and magical happenings. "The Snow Maiden" is one of the oldest and best-loved fairy tales of Russia. That story is full of the magic of the changing seasons and the coming of spring.

"How the Pig and the Bear Went into Business" is a short and silly folk tale from Czechoslovakia about two animals who are very good friends—but who need a lesson about doing business! "The Pied Piper of Hamelin" is also a folk tale, this time from Germany. There's a lesson here too: about keeping promises and being honest.

Happy reading—and enjoy your visit to Europe!

# The Arrival of Paddington

## ALFRED BRADLEY and MICHAEL BOND

### CAST OF CHARACTERS

MR. BROWN     PADDINGTON BEAR     JUDY BROWN

MRS. BROWN     REFRESHMENT MAN

SCENE: *The play takes place in Paddington Station. All that you need is a heap of parcels to hide* PADDINGTON *(cardboard boxes will do) and a sign saying "Paddington Station."* PADDINGTON *wears a floppy bush hat and Wellington boots, and has a label tied around his neck which says, "Please look after this bear. Thank you." In his suitcase, which he takes with him wherever he goes, is a jar of marmalade. When the refreshment man arrives, he should have a tea cart or a tray with several plastic or paper cups and some sticky cakes. (As real cakes may be messy, it is probably best to make your own out of shaving cream, which will wash off easily.) The sticky cake wrapper can be made out of waxed paper or plastic wrap covered with double-sided, transparent sticky tape.*

    *When the play begins,* PADDINGTON *is concealed behind an assorted pile of parcels and luggage.* HENRY BROWN *comes onto the platform, closely followed by his wife.*

MR. BROWN: Well, Mary, after all that rushing about, we're here early.

MRS. BROWN: What's the time now?

MR. BROWN: It's just a quarter past four, and Judy's train doesn't arrive until half past.

11

MRS. BROWN: Are you sure?

MR. BROWN: She told me in her letter, and she doesn't usually make mistakes.

MRS. BROWN: I'll just go and check which platform . . . (*She goes off. Left to himself* MR. BROWN *strolls around the platform.* PADDINGTON, *hidden behind the parcels, pops up like a jack-in-the-box and quickly down again.* MR. BROWN *is looking surprised;* MRS. BROWN *returns.*)

MRS. BROWN: It's platform five. And you're quite right—the train doesn't arrive until half past four.

MR. BROWN: Mary, you won't believe this, but I've just seen a bear.

MRS. BROWN: A what?

MR. BROWN: A bear.

MRS. BROWN: A bear? In Paddington Station? Don't be silly, Henry. There can't be.

MR. BROWN: But there is. I distinctly saw it. Over there. Behind those parcels. It was wearing a funny kind of hat. Come and see for yourself.

MRS. BROWN: (*humoring him*) Very well. (*She peers behind the parcels.*) Why Henry, I believe you were right after all. It is a bear!
(PADDINGTON *stands up suddenly. He is wearing a bush hat with a wide brim and has a large luggage label around his neck.*)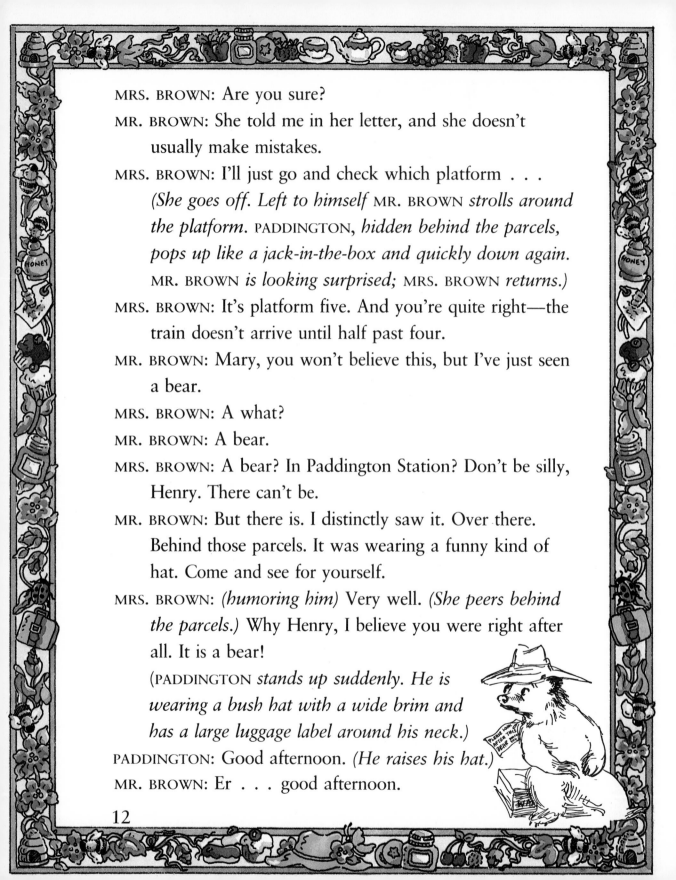

PADDINGTON: Good afternoon. (*He raises his hat.*)

MR. BROWN: Er . . . good afternoon.

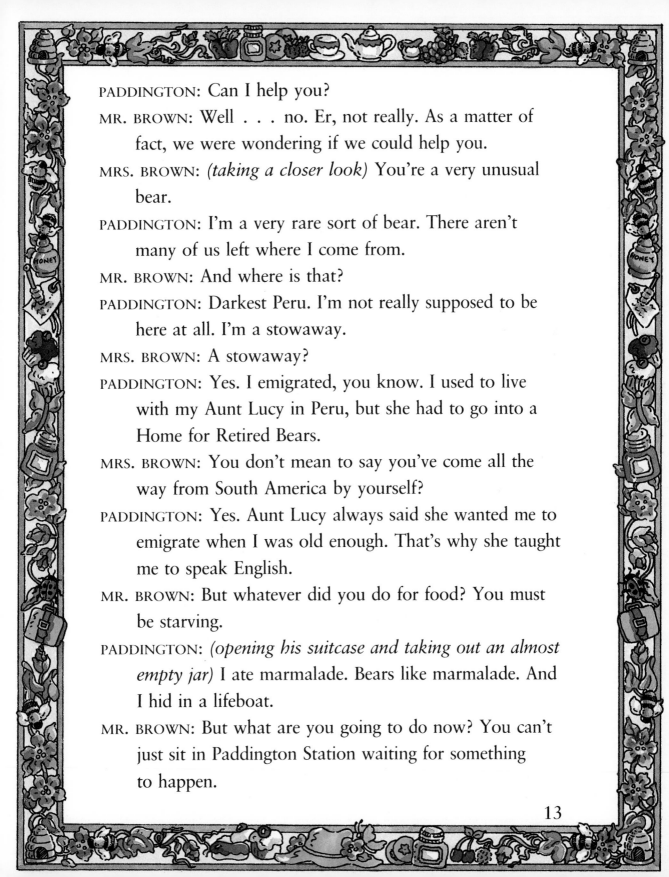

PADDINGTON: Can I help you?

MR. BROWN: Well . . . no. Er, not really. As a matter of fact, we were wondering if we could help you.

MRS. BROWN: *(taking a closer look)* You're a very unusual bear.

PADDINGTON: I'm a very rare sort of bear. There aren't many of us left where I come from.

MR. BROWN: And where is that?

PADDINGTON: Darkest Peru. I'm not really supposed to be here at all. I'm a stowaway.

MRS. BROWN: A stowaway?

PADDINGTON: Yes. I emigrated, you know. I used to live with my Aunt Lucy in Peru, but she had to go into a Home for Retired Bears.

MRS. BROWN: You don't mean to say you've come all the way from South America by yourself?

PADDINGTON: Yes. Aunt Lucy always said she wanted me to emigrate when I was old enough. That's why she taught me to speak English.

MR. BROWN: But whatever did you do for food? You must be starving.

PADDINGTON: *(opening his suitcase and taking out an almost empty jar)* I ate marmalade. Bears like marmalade. And I hid in a lifeboat.

MR. BROWN: But what are you going to do now? You can't just sit in Paddington Station waiting for something to happen.

13

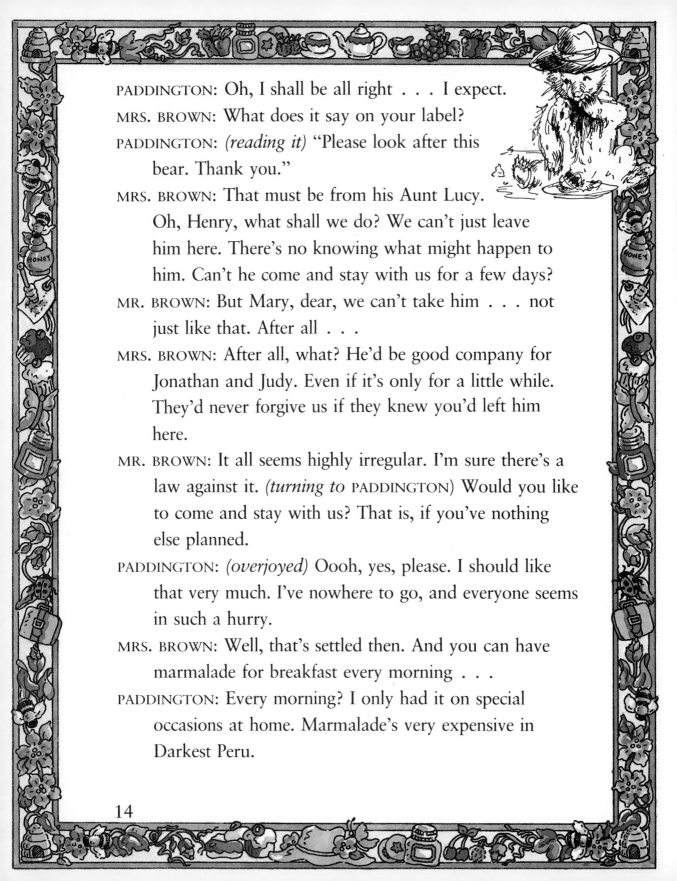

PADDINGTON: Oh, I shall be all right . . . I expect.

MRS. BROWN: What does it say on your label?

PADDINGTON: *(reading it)* "Please look after this bear. Thank you."

MRS. BROWN: That must be from his Aunt Lucy. Oh, Henry, what shall we do? We can't just leave him here. There's no knowing what might happen to him. Can't he come and stay with us for a few days?

MR. BROWN: But Mary, dear, we can't take him . . . not just like that. After all . . .

MRS. BROWN: After all, what? He'd be good company for Jonathan and Judy. Even if it's only for a little while. They'd never forgive us if they knew you'd left him here.

MR. BROWN: It all seems highly irregular. I'm sure there's a law against it. *(turning to* PADDINGTON*)* Would you like to come and stay with us? That is, if you've nothing else planned.

PADDINGTON: *(overjoyed)* Oooh, yes, please. I should like that very much. I've nowhere to go, and everyone seems in such a hurry.

MRS. BROWN: Well, that's settled then. And you can have marmalade for breakfast every morning . . .

PADDINGTON: Every morning? I only had it on special occasions at home. Marmalade's very expensive in Darkest Peru.

14

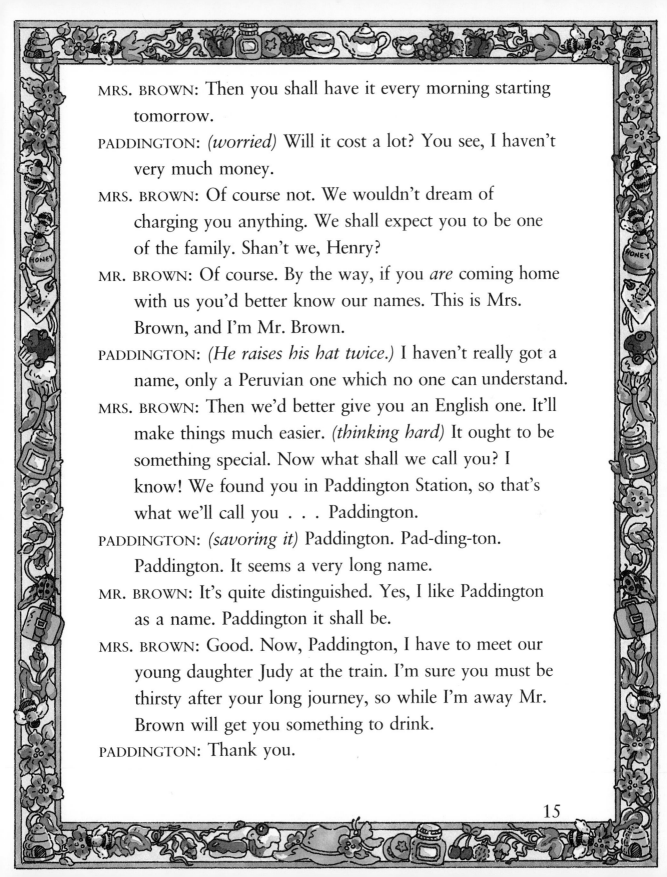

MRS. BROWN: Then you shall have it every morning starting tomorrow.

PADDINGTON: *(worried)* Will it cost a lot? You see, I haven't very much money.

MRS. BROWN: Of course not. We wouldn't dream of charging you anything. We shall expect you to be one of the family. Shan't we, Henry?

MR. BROWN: Of course. By the way, if you *are* coming home with us you'd better know our names. This is Mrs. Brown, and I'm Mr. Brown.

PADDINGTON: *(He raises his hat twice.)* I haven't really got a name, only a Peruvian one which no one can understand.

MRS. BROWN: Then we'd better give you an English one. It'll make things much easier. *(thinking hard)* It ought to be something special. Now what shall we call you? I know! We found you in Paddington Station, so that's what we'll call you . . . Paddington.

PADDINGTON: *(savoring it)* Paddington. Pad-ding-ton. Paddington. It seems a very long name.

MR. BROWN: It's quite distinguished. Yes, I like Paddington as a name. Paddington it shall be.

MRS. BROWN: Good. Now, Paddington, I have to meet our young daughter Judy at the train. I'm sure you must be thirsty after your long journey, so while I'm away Mr. Brown will get you something to drink.

PADDINGTON: Thank you.

MRS. BROWN: And for goodness sake, Henry, when you get a moment, take that label off his neck. It makes him look like a parcel. (PADDINGTON *doesn't much like the thought of looking like a parcel.*) I'm sure he'll get put in a luggage van if a porter sees him. (*She goes off, almost bumping into a* MAN *pushing the refreshment cart.*)

MR. BROWN: (*removing the label*) There we are. Ah! The very thing. Now I can get you something to drink. (PADDINGTON *puts the luggage label into his suitcase.*)

MAN: What would you like, tea or coffee?

PADDINGTON: Cocoa, please.

MAN: (*annoyed*) We haven't got any cocoa.

PADDINGTON: But you asked me what I would like . . .

MAN: I asked you what you would like, *tea* or *coffee!*

MR. BROWN: (*hastily, trying to avoid an argument*) Perhaps you'd like a cold drink?

MAN: Lemonade or orangeade?

PADDINGTON: Marmalade.

MR. BROWN: (*before the* MAN *loses his temper*) I think some orangeade would be a good idea—and a cup of tea for me, please. (*The* MAN *serves them.*) And perhaps you'd like a cake, Paddington?

PADDINGTON: Oooh, yes, please.

MAN: Cream-and-chocolate or cream-and-jam?

PADDINGTON: Yes, please.

MAN: Well, which do you want?

MR. BROWN: We'd better have some of each.

(The MAN *puts four cakes on a plate.* MR. BROWN *pays him and hands the plate to* PADDINGTON.) How's that?

PADDINGTON: It's very nice, thank you, Mr. Brown, but it's not very easy drinking out of a cup. I usually get my nose stuck.

MR. BROWN: Perhaps you'd like a straw. (He takes one from the MAN and puts it into PADDINGTON's cup.)

PADDINGTON: That's a good idea. (He blows through the straw and makes a bubbling sound.) I'm glad I emigrated. (He takes a bite from one of the cakes.) I wonder what else there is?

(He puts the plate of cakes on the floor in order to peer at the cart and promptly steps on the plate. In his excitement he upsets the cups on the cart, scattering them in all directions. Trying to steady himself, he knocks MR. BROWN's tea out of his hand, slips over, and ends up sprawled on the platform. As MR. BROWN bends to help him up, PADDINGTON staggers to his feet with one of the cakes stuck to his paw. They collide, and the cake ends up plastered all over MR. BROWN's face. Just at this moment MRS. BROWN returns with JUDY.)

MRS. BROWN: Henry! Henry, whatever are you doing to that poor bear? Look at him!

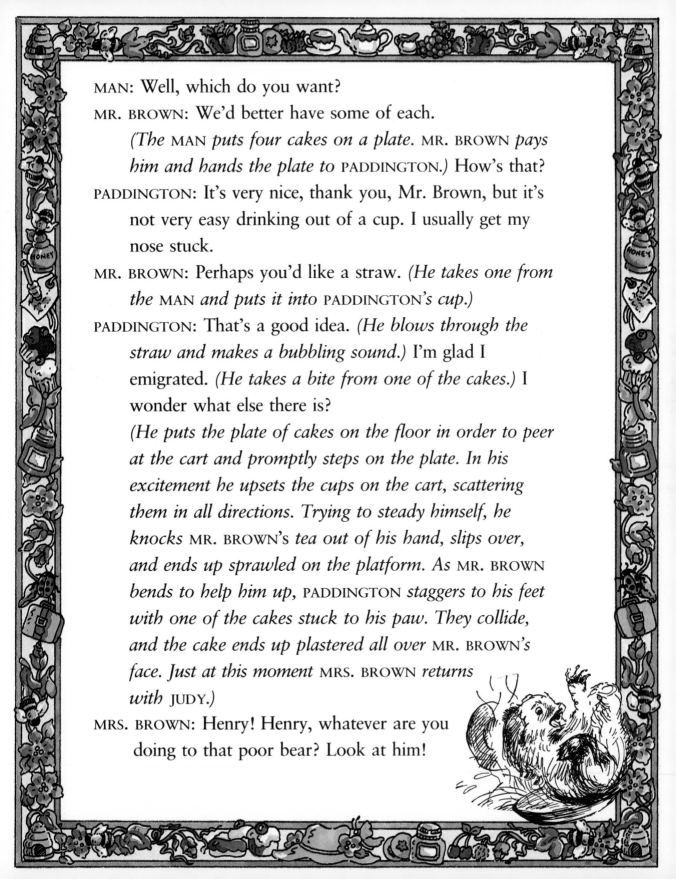

He's covered all over with jam and cream.

MR. BROWN: *He's* covered with jam and cream! What about me? *(He begins to tidy up the mess.)*

MRS. BROWN: This is what happens when I leave your father alone for five minutes.

JUDY: *(clapping her hands)* Oh, Daddy, is he really going to stay with us? (PADDINGTON *stands up, raises his hat, steps on the plate of cakes again and falls over.)* Oh, Mummy, isn't he funny!

MRS. BROWN: You wouldn't think that anybody could get into such a state with cakes.

MR. BROWN: Perhaps we'd better go. Are we all ready?

JUDY: Come along, Paddington. (PADDINGTON *picks up his suitcase and opens it to put the remains of the cakes in it. A cake wrapper sticks to his paws but he doesn't notice it.)* We'll go straight home, and you can have a nice hot bath. Then you can tell me all about South America. I'm sure you must have had lots of wonderful adventures.

PADDINGTON: I have. Lots. Things are always happening to me—I'm that sort of bear. *(He goes off with* JUDY.*)*

MR. BROWN: *(to his wife)* I hope we haven't bitten off more than we can chew.

MAN: Well, if you have, you'll just have to grin and *bear* it. *(He laughs loudly at his own joke and goes off.)*

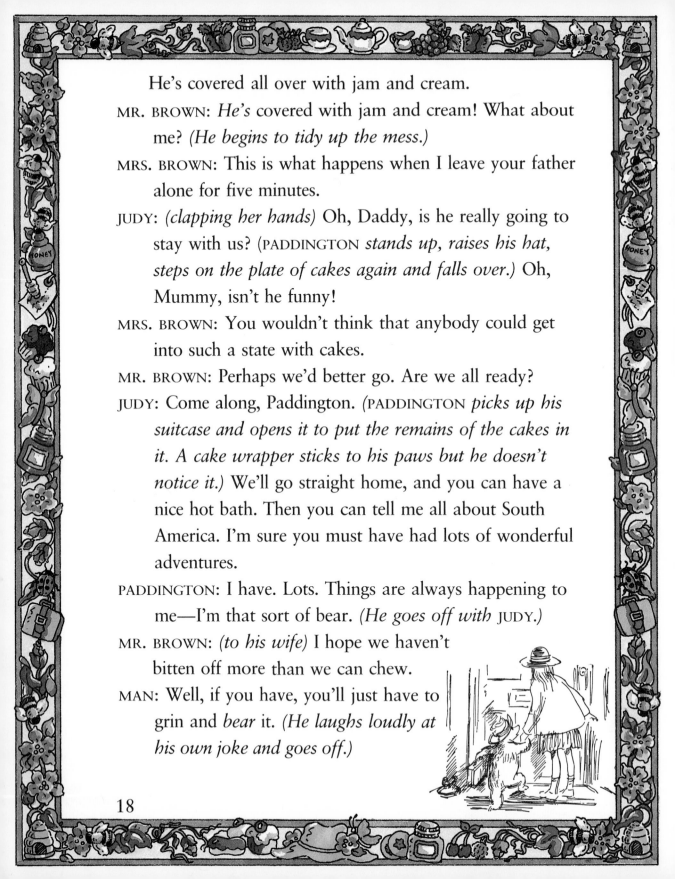

18

# The Land of Counterpane

ROBERT LOUIS STEVENSON

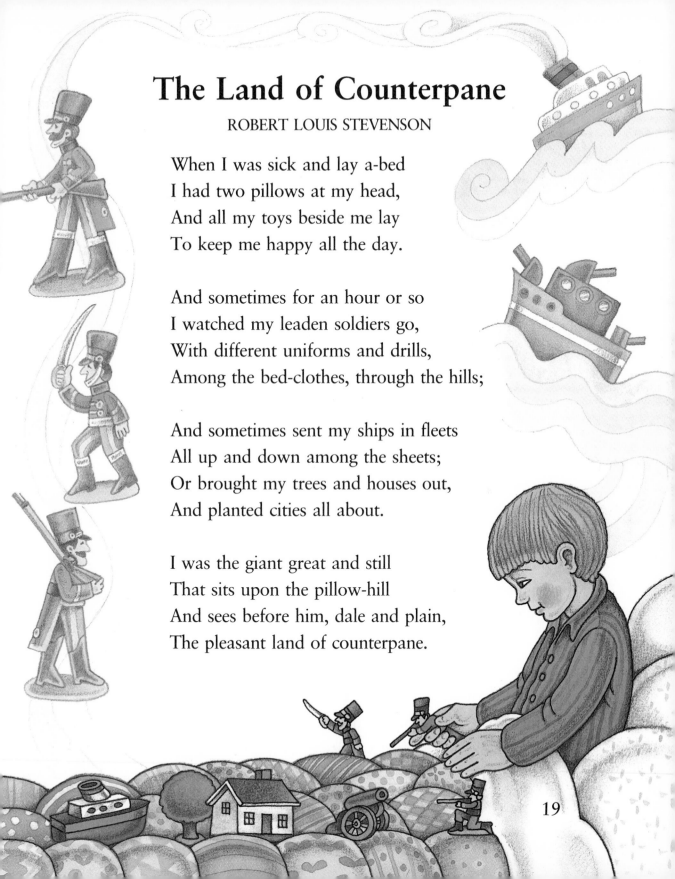

When I was sick and lay a-bed
I had two pillows at my head,
And all my toys beside me lay
To keep me happy all the day.

And sometimes for an hour or so
I watched my leaden soldiers go,
With different uniforms and drills,
Among the bed-clothes, through the hills;

And sometimes sent my ships in fleets
All up and down among the sheets;
Or brought my trees and houses out,
And planted cities all about.

I was the giant great and still
That sits upon the pillow-hill
And sees before him, dale and plain,
The pleasant land of counterpane.

19

# To Sail a Ship of Treasures

LISL WEIL

We are all sailing on a ship that moves ahead with us every day. It is a ship with room to store all the treasures we find as we sail on and on and on. The ship is our life, and the treasures are the memories we store there for ourselves.

Here are a few of my own very special treasures. I want to share them with you.

I was born on the other side of the great Atlantic Ocean, in the country of Austria in the city of Vienna. The earliest thing I remember is feeling snug and safe. My parents loved me.

When I was still very young, I remember going for a long vacation in the country, with my mother and my big sister. When we came back to the city, we lived in a new apartment, with a ting-a-ling chandelier that made me think of a fairy palace.

I had a friend named Berta, who lived in the apartment building. We both liked to draw. Berta always drew dresses. I liked to draw people, especially sailors and places a sailor might go.

When I was six years old, I started school. What I liked best was drawing and learning to read. Soon I was the fastest reader in the class.

At about the same time, I started taking dancing lessons from a famous dancer. I loved dancing. Our class began by dancing to a polonaise by Chopin. Then we did other group dances, waltzes, and ballet. At the end of each lesson, we could each dance whatever we wanted to dance. Such joy! I felt as if I never wanted to stop dancing.

Our family always got together for Sunday dinner at one o'clock. After dinner, my dad and I would dance a *czardas* while my sister played the piano. My dad was Hungarian, and the czardas is a Hungarian dance.

I had a dog, two white rabbits, and two birds as pets. I loved them very much. When I came home from school one day, one of my birds looked different. I wanted to believe that it was the same Hansi. (All the birds were called Hansi.) But inside I knew that one of my birds had died and my mother had gotten me a new one because she didn't want me to be sad.

One day I became very ill. I was so sick that doctors came from everywhere to look at me while I lay in bed. Some of their treatments hurt very much, but none of them helped. I heard them say to my mother, "This child will die."

But my mother did not want me to die. She loved me too much. She stayed by my bedside night and day. And I did not die. It was her love that made me well again. My mother was beautiful, outside and inside.

I was sick for more than a year. I even had to learn to walk all over again. But finally I was ready to go back to school. When I went to school, I did not know that I looked different. But I soon found out. The children pointed at me and laughed.

After I got home, I took a good look at myself. And I did look funny. My illness has left me with a crooked face.

But my family loved me just the same, and I got used to looking different.

Crooked face and all, I sailed on to new things, good and bad, to store away with my remembered treasures.

I became very busy. I still liked reading and drawing, and I took piano lessons and French lessons. I started dancing lessons again, too.

Because I wanted more money to buy books, I began to draw picture cards that I hoped to sell. The owner of the shop where I bought books said she would display them and pay me if she sold any. My dad was my first customer. But other people bought them, too. I felt proud.

Every day, after he closed his shop, my dad would meet his friends at his favorite coffee house. A coffee house in Vienna is a very special place. When I was twelve years old, he took my mother and me there for frankfurters with sweet horseradish. I can still taste it. It was wonderful. But best of all, the coffee house had magazines and newspapers from all over the world for everyone to look at and read. Some I could understand, others I could not.

I was fourteen when a magazine first printed one of my drawings. Soon I was making a drawing every week for that magazine and also for a daily paper. My mother was so proud that she called her best friend every time a picture appeared. My dad showed the magazine and paper to all of his friends at the coffee house. He was proud, too.

My world was wonderful. I sailed ahead happily collecting treasures to remember.

Yet not all memories are good. My dad got very, very sick. On a beautiful day, with blossoms perfuming the air (I can still smell them) and birds chirping, he died. I could not understand how so much sadness could come on such a joyous day.

Other things happened that year that I could not understand. A new leader and a new order began to change my world. Large groups of people began to hate other groups of people. If you did not belong to the right group, you and your family could be destroyed.

One needed good luck to get away. I was lucky. After a stopover at another country—where I could even do drawings to support myself—a big ship brought me to a fine new world.

I landed in New York no longer a child. Yet, like a child, I had to learn a new language and learn how to live in a new place. My sister had arrived before me. My mother arrived two years later, but she lived for only a few weeks more.

Good or sad, everything one remembers is important. Our memories help make us the people we are. Each of us has different things to remember, different things to wonder about, different people to recall and to love.

You too are sailing ahead each day and have your own very special ship of treasures. They make your very own story.

# Beauty and the Beast

A FRENCH FAIRY TALE

## [ PART 1 ]

Once upon a time there lived a very rich merchant who had three sons and three daughters. The girls were all beautiful, but the youngest was so lovely that she was called Beauty. This made her sisters very jealous.

Beauty was not only prettier than her sisters, but she was also smarter than they were. And unlike them, she was both helpful and kind. The sisters hated her for her kind heart and laughed at her because she spent her time reading good books instead of going to parties and balls as they did.

Suddenly, misfortune came to Beauty's father. He lost all of his money in business and every one of his ships at sea. All he had left was a small farm in the country. There he and his sons worked in the fields. Beauty got up each day at dawn. She lit the fires, cleaned the house, and prepared the meals. Though it was hard work, Beauty never complained. Her sisters, however, did nothing but complain. They did no work themselves, but just watching Beauty made them cross.

After a year, news came that one of their father's ships had not been lost but, filled to the top with riches, had

sailed safely into port. Before he left to meet the ship, the older sisters asked their father to bring back some jewels and dresses for them. Beauty did not ask for anything.

"What shall I bring for you, Beauty?" her father asked.

"The only wish I have is to see you come home safely," she answered.

"But surely there is something you would like to have," said her father.

"Well, dear Father, then bring me a rose," said Beauty. "I love roses very much, and I have not seen one for a very long time."

In town, the merchant used most of the money from the ship's cargo to pay old debts. He started home as poor as when he had left. Deep snow and bitter frost made it impossible for his horse to carry him home that evening.

Night fell, and wolves were howling all around him. The merchant had lost his way in the deep forest, when suddenly he saw lights shining among the trees. When he hurried closer, he saw a magnificent castle standing in a beautiful park. He went through the open gate, got off his horse, and entered the castle. He saw nobody and heard not a sound.

The merchant sat down in front of a friendly fire, where a delicious dinner was waiting for him. He ate the dinner with much pleasure and hoped that he could soon thank his good host, but nobody appeared. He fell asleep after his meal and did not wake up until late the next morning. Next to him he saw a fine new suit in place of his old one.

"A kind fairy must own this castle," the merchant thought, but he did not see or hear any sign of life in the whole palace. Finally he went down into the lovely garden, where birds were singing and flowers were blooming. The beautiful roses reminded him of Beauty's wish, and he picked one of them.

Just then he heard a terrible roar, and a frightful Beast rushed up. It seemed to be very angry and said in a terrible voice, "Why are you stealing my roses? Did I not shelter you in my palace? Is this the way you say thank you? For this I shall kill you!"

The merchant was terrified. He threw himself on his knees and begged for mercy.

"I meant no harm, Your Majesty. I took the rose for one of my daughters. She asked me to bring her one. Please forgive me, Your Majesty."

"My name is not Majesty," roared the creature. "My name is Beast. I do not like to be flattered. Go home to your daughters. Ask whether one of them is willing to die for you. If they refuse, you must return yourself."

The merchant turned pale at the thought, but he promised to come back. He thought, I'll go and say farewell to my family. He found his horse already saddled, and soon he was home. He gave Beauty the rose and said, "Beauty, here is your rose. I had to pay a high price for it."

Then he told his daughters all that had happened. The older daughters wept loudly and begged their father not to go back. But Beauty said, "You have to keep your promise to the Beast, and I will go with you, dear Father."

But her father shook his head. "I will not let you go. I will go alone. I am old, and I shall die soon anyway."

Beauty stood firm. "Father, I *must* go," she said. "I would die of grief if I caused your death."

So Beauty said good-bye to her sisters and brothers and bravely mounted the horse with her father. Soon they reached the palace. In the dining hall they found a table set for two with golden plates, crystal glasses, and delicious food. They sat down to eat. Beauty thought, The Beast wants to fatten me up so that I will taste better when he eats me.

After dinner they heard the Beast's footsteps coming closer and closer. Beauty trembled and clung to her father. The Beast entered with a loud roar. Beauty was certain that

he would eat her, but she tried to hide her fear and greeted
him politely.

"Did you come willingly?" asked the Beast in his
terrible voice.

"Yes," answered Beauty.

"You are very good. I am pleased with you," said the
Beast. "Your father must leave tomorrow, and he can never
come back. Good night, Beauty."

"Good night, Beast," she said.

Beauty went to bed, and as she slept that night, she saw
a beautiful fairy in her dreams. The fairy said, "Beauty, you
have a good heart, and you shall be rewarded."

## [ PART 2 ]

After her father had left the next morning, Beauty wept.
She thought that the Beast would surely eat her this very night.

30

Bravely she tried not to worry. "I'll enjoy my last day and explore the palace," she said to herself. She walked through many rooms. She found each one more brilliant than the last, until finally she came to a door marked *Beauty's Apartment.*

She opened the door timidly, and there she saw the room of her dreams. There were shelves of books, a piano, music, beautiful needlework for her to do, and everything else she could wish for. That night, as she sat down to supper, she heard the Beast coming. She began to tremble, for she wondered if he meant to eat her now.

The Beast only said gruffly, "Good evening, Beauty," and sat down and kept her company during the dinner.

"Everything here is yours," he said after a while. "Your wish is law. I hope that you will be happy here. I am only a stupid Beast. Tell me, do you find me very ugly?"

"Yes," said Beauty. "I cannot lie, but I think you are also very good and kind and not stupid at all."

Beauty had almost forgotten to be afraid of the monster when he asked her, "Do you love me, Beauty? Will you marry me?"

Beauty was silent. At last she said honestly, "No, Beast, I cannot marry you."

The Beast sighed deeply and then left the room.

Three months passed. Beauty had everything she could wish for. She had become used to the ugliness of the Beast.

She even looked forward to the evenings, when he always came to talk to her. He was so good and kind that she liked him more and more.

Every night he asked her to marry him. One night Beauty said, "Beast, you are my best friend, and you are very dear to me, but I don't think I shall ever be able to marry you."

"Beauty," said the Beast, "I will die without you. Please promise that you will never leave me." Beauty became very sad. She was very homesick for her father and longed to see him once more. She begged the Beast to let her go.

"Please let me go home for a week, Beast. We are good friends, and I promise to come back."

"Very well. I cannot let you suffer," said the Beast. "But if you are not back in one week, your faithful Beast will die. When you are ready to come back, you have only to turn your ring on your finger." And the Beast sighed even more loudly than usual.

The next morning when Beauty woke up, she was in her father's house. She dressed in the gold and diamond gown that the kind Beast had sent, and she went to greet her father. How happy the merchant was when he saw his daughter! He hugged and kissed her and laughed and cried for joy all at the same time.

Beauty's brothers had joined the army, but her sisters, who were married now and who lived close by, came to see her.

They were not at all happy to see Beauty dressed like a queen, looking lovelier than ever before. In their jealousy they planned to keep her longer than seven days so that she would break her promise to the Beast.

"Perhaps then he will eat her," they said. They treated Beauty so well and put on such a show of kindness that Beauty agreed to stay another week.

On the tenth night, Beauty dreamed that the Beast was lying on the grass in his garden, dying of despair. "Oh, my poor Beast," she cried. "He cannot help being ugly. He has a good and kind heart, and that is worth more than anything."

She turned her ring on her finger and at once found herself back in her beautiful palace. She looked everywhere for her Beast. Then she remembered her dream, and she ran into the garden. There lay the Beast, quite still.

"What if I have killed him?" thought Beauty, terrified.

Beauty forgot the Beast's ugliness and bent over him. His heart was still beating faintly. Suddenly he opened his eyes. He whispered to her, "I cannot live without you. Now that you are here, I will die happy."

"No, Beast, you cannot die," cried Beauty. "I never knew how much I loved you until now. I was afraid that I was too late to save your life. I cannot live without you, dear Beast. Let me be your wife."

As Beauty spoke these words, a blaze of light sprang up

through the whole palace. Music filled the air. Suddenly the Beast disappeared, and in his place stood a handsome prince.

"Where is my Beast?" cried Beauty.

"I am he," answered the prince. "I was turned into a Beast by a powerful witch. Only a beautiful girl who would love me for my kind heart could break the spell. Only you could help me, for you love goodness more than beauty and riches. Please, Beauty, be my queen."

Beauty gave the prince her hand, and he led her into the castle. There Beauty found her father and all her family. The fairy who had appeared in Beauty's dream had brought them all there. What joy and happiness!

"Beauty," said the fairy, "you will be a great queen. You will find beauty, wisdom, and goodness in the prince, who loves you. This is the reward for your good heart."

Beauty and her prince were married in great splendor, and they lived happily ever after.

# How the Pig and the Bear Went into Business

## A CZECH FOLK TALE
Retold by VÍT HOŘEJŠ

The pig and the bear decided to go into business. "We'll make lots of money!" they said to themselves.

The pig baked a bushel of potatoes, and the bear fried a heap of doughnuts.

They went to the marketplace early in the morning to get the best spots. Nobody was around yet. The morning was clear and chilly. The bear had a nickel in his coat. After a while he went over to the pig's stand to warm up a little.

"How much for a potato?" he growled.

"A nickel for you."

The bear was about to say that he'd just wanted to ask, but then he changed his mind. He fished for the nickel in his fur, took the biggest steaming potato in his paws, and crossed the road back to his stand.

The business is moving, rejoiced the pig. But there were no more customers for a while, and she hadn't eaten since they started at dawn, so she crossed over to the bear's stand and bought herself a black-raspberry doughnut for a nickel.

The bear was happy to make his first sale. He felt he should eat something before the customers started to flock to his stand, so he went over to buy another baked potato. The move brought him luck. He had hardly finished eating when the pig was over for another doughnut.

Then business slacked off again until the bear bought a potato. Soon the pig was over again, and the bear went right back with her to her stand to spend the earned nickel. The pig returned for a doughnut, and soon they were going back and forth until they had sold everything.

They counted the money—but, strangely, the bear had only a nickel, and the pig had nothing at all. They couldn't believe it.

"We have sold all our merchandise," they kept saying, "but we have no money."

In vain they counted and recounted: they had only a nickel between them after the whole day of busy trading.

# The Snow Maiden

## A RUSSIAN FAIRY TALE

Many years ago there lived an old woman and an old man
in a little log hut. As they grew older, they also grew sadder,
for they had no children.

One winter morning the old man looked out the
window and saw snow falling. Soon he saw the village boys
and girls playing outside, sliding on their sleds and throwing
snowballs. After a while, they all began making a snowman.

As the old man watched them, he turned to the old
woman and said, "Why don't we go outside and make a
snowman too?"

"Very well," said the old woman, "but instead of a snowman, let us make a daughter of snow, a snow maiden."

So they went out into the garden and began to make a little girl out of snow. They made the legs, the arms, and the head. They used bits of sparkling ice for the eyes, and they even made the eyebrows.

When the old man and old woman had finished, they could hardly believe that they had made such a beautiful snow maiden.

Suddenly the snow maiden began to smile. Then she moved her eyebrows, raised her arms, and began to walk quietly along the snow toward the hut.

The old man and old woman were overjoyed, and they ran after her into the hut. They prepared a delicious meal for their guest and showed her the comfortable bed where she would sleep. They spared no trouble in making her feel welcome in their home.

And so it came to pass that the little snow maiden stayed with the old man and the old woman. Each day she became more lovely and more dear. The old man and old woman were completely delighted with her. They bought her lovely clothes and beautiful slippers with pretty satin bows on them.

The days passed, until winter came to an end and spring arrived. The sun began to warm the earth, and the water in the brooks began to flow again. All the children were joyous at the coming of spring.

Only the snow maiden was unhappy. She sat in the corner of the hut and would not look out the window. The only time she was happy was when dark clouds covered the sky and a cold wind blew.

The old woman looked at her and shook her head. "What is the trouble, little daughter?"

"It is nothing, dear Mother."

"Are you ill, perhaps?"

The snow maiden was silent, but tears were rolling down her cheeks.

Spring seemed to pass by quickly, and then summer arrived. The sun was hot, and the flowers were blooming. One day the girls of the village gathered to take a walk in the woods. They called to the snow maiden, "Come with us!"

But the snow maiden was afraid to step outside the door. "It is hot," she said. "The sun will bake my head."

The old woman persuaded her to go out. "Go on, little daughter. Why do you shut yourself in all alone?"

So the snow maiden obeyed and went off with the girls, who picked flowers in the woods and wove garlands. The snow maiden, however, sat in the shade beside a cool brook and dangled her feet in the water until sunset.

Finally the sun went down, and evening came. The girls were having a gay time. They built a bonfire, and then one of them got the idea of jumping over the flames. She jumped, and then another girl jumped, and then a third. Finally the snow maiden's turn came, but she would not jump over the flames.

"Why don't you jump?" her friends said to her. "Are you afraid?" Then they began to laugh at her.

The snow maiden gathered her courage, ran toward the flames, and jumped. As the girls watched, she disappeared into a white mist above the bonfire. The mist formed itself into a thin cloud and rose higher and higher until it joined the clouds in the sky.

The old man and the old woman wept bitterly when their dear little snow maiden did not return home that evening. They looked for her everywhere and waited every night for her. But the snow maiden did not come back. They were sad and lonely, talking and thinking only about their little daughter, whom they had loved so much.

After a while, the days became shorter and the nights longer. The air was crisp and cool once again. Winter was coming.

One night, when the first snow was falling, the old man and the old woman heard a happy laugh outside their hut and a dear, familiar voice singing:

Winter is here,
I am back with the snow,
But please do not fear
In summer when I go.

They ran to the door, and there was their little daughter, their snow maiden. How happy they all were to be together again! She stayed with them all winter long and played with the other children of the village.

When summer came and the sun was hot again, the snow maiden disappeared once more. The old man and the old woman were not so sad this time, however. They knew that every winter when the snow began to fall, their little snow maiden would return to live with them and bring them all the joy and happiness they could wish for.

# The Pied Piper of Hamelin

A GERMAN FOLK TALE
Retold by TONY ROSS

Long, long ago, when towns were very small, the people of Hamelin lived in fear and misery. The town itself was pretty enough, with lots of cakeshops and with parks to play in. Yet the people crept about the streets, peering this way and that, jumping at the slightest sound.

The reason for this unhappy state of affairs was *rats!* Millions of rats lived in Hamelin. They were large, fat rats, with big teeth and nasty tempers. Nobody knew why there were so many rats; perhaps it was because Hamelin was such a nice place to live that all of the rats in Germany moved there. They prowled the streets in gangs, squeaking and generally making nuisances of themselves. They chased the cats and the dogs. They jumped out of holes in the walls and danced up and down on the furniture. They nested in people's best clothes. They even ate the cakes in the shop windows.

The mayor and the town council tried all ways to rid Hamelin of the rats. They met every Tuesday to argue over new ideas. They invented all sorts of traps. They even built a clockwork cat with big iron teeth and fast wheels. But nothing ever worked.

The mayor didn't know what to do about the rats, but the people of Hamelin expected him to do *something!*

One day, the mayor and the council were holding a meeting on the table. They often met on the table because of the rats on the floor. Suddenly they noticed a stranger standing by the door. His clothes were half red and half yellow. A flute was tucked into his belt. He spoke politely, in a soft voice. "Sirs, I have heard tell of your rats, and for a thousand gold pieces I can rid your town of them."

"Yes, yes!" cried the mayor and council together, wobbling on the table.

Putting his pipe to his lips, the Piper started to play a thin, magical tune. The rats stopped teasing the town council and looked around, blissful smiles on their nasty faces. The Piper turned and stepped into the street, the rats skipping along behind him to the tune of the pipe. Through

the streets he strode, followed by a horde of rats that danced out of every nook and cranny. The mayor and council watched in amazement as the Pied Piper disappeared through the town gate with his squealing, leaping company.

The mad procession took the road toward the River Weser. On reaching the water's edge, the Piper crouched on a boulder. His music quickened as the rats streamed past, slipping and sliding on the river bank. In their hundreds the rats danced into the river, to be swirled away in the fast waters and drowned.

However, one rat, who was a little deaf and could hear only snatches of the Piper's tune, kept her wits about her. She managed to scramble to safety on a rock, but she didn't return to the town. Instead, she took to the road and warned every rat she met of the terrible things that happened to rats in Hamelin.

His work done, the Pied Piper returned to Hamelin to claim his thousand pieces of gold. The mayor was not an

honest man, however. Seeing that all the rats had gone, he saw no reason to pay the Piper.

Angered at being cheated, the Piper pointed a quivering finger at the mayor. "This is one promise you will regret breaking!" he snapped. Putting his pipe to his lips, the Piper turned on his heel and stormed back into the street.

Once more the Pied Piper strode through Hamelin, playing a wild tune, his cloak streaming out behind him. The mayor watched in horror, unable to move, as children began to follow the music. They stopped their games. They climbed out of their windows, drawn by the sound of the enchanted pipe. The Piper headed for the river, but at the last minute he swung away to the west.

Night was falling when the Piper halted the children at a mountain. At an unheard command, a huge door opened in the mountainside and, laughing and dancing, the children disappeared inside. The door closed as mysteriously as it had opened. The Piper tucked his pipe into his belt and melted into the silence.

Not all of Hamelin's children were locked inside the mountain. One little boy, Jan, was lame and couldn't dance as fast as the rest. Unnoticed, Jan had followed on behind. It was dark when he reached the mountain; he had followed the footprints in the dust and the faint sounds of the music.

In the moonlight, he stood and stared at the bare hillside where the tracks ended. Then sadly, and all alone, Jan turned and limped back to Hamelin.

Poor Jan was the only child left in Hamelin. As he had no one to play with, all the grown-ups made a great fuss over him. They listened again and again to his story of how the children had vanished into the mountain.

From that day on, the townspeople waited in vain for their children to return. And the mayor? Well, he bitterly regretted the day he had tried to cheat the Pied Piper of Hamelin.

# Unit Two
## The Mediterranean

# The Mediterranean

For thousands of years the Mediterranean Sea has played an important part in human history. This great sea lies south of Europe and borders on three continents—Europe, Asia, and Africa. Long ago, the people who lived along the Mediterranean thought that their lands were the only lands in the world. The great sea in the middle, therefore, had to have been the center of all the land in the world. So they named the sea the Mediterranean, which means "middle of the world."

Egypt is one of the countries bordering the Mediterranean Sea. It is in the continent of Africa and is the home of one of the oldest civilizations in the world. While other people were still living in caves, Egyptians were building large cities, developing new tools, raising crops, studying the stars, and writing books using their beautiful hieroglyphics. The story called "The Dead King" will tell you how many of the secrets of ancient Egypt have been discovered deep within the pyramids and in the hidden tombs of Egyptian kings. Then, in "You've Come a Long Way, Kitty!", you'll learn how cats first came to be pets in Egypt—and why the Egyptians thought cats were magical beings!

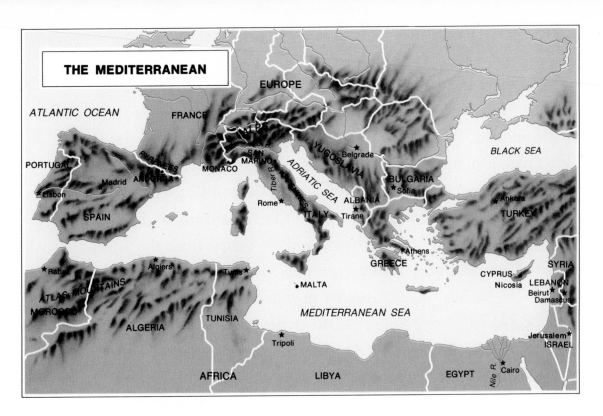

Long after the ancient Egyptian civilization ended, another important civilization developed along the Mediterranean in Greece. Some of the world's greatest scientists, writers, and artists lived in Greece over two thousand years ago. It was in Greece that the idea of democracy, or government by the people, was born. Many stories about the Greek world, and about the gods and goddesses the Greeks believed in, still exist today as myths. You will read about one of these myths in "The Golden Touch."

The Greeks were conquered by the Romans, whose empire was the largest in the world for hundreds of years. The Romans ruled millions of people who spoke many different languages and held many different beliefs. The Romans were great builders and lawmakers. Many of their buildings, bridges, and roads are still standing today, and the laws of many modern countries are based on those of the Roman Empire. "Black Cloud from Vesuvius" tells about life in the Roman seaside town of Herculaneum, and how a young girl and her family make their escape from the angry volcano erupting from deep inside Mount Vesuvius.

The Arabs were another group of early Mediterranean people who were important to civilizations who came after them. The Arabs made discoveries in science, mathematics, and medicine. They kept copies of famous Greek and Roman writings in their libraries, saving these works for later civilizations.

Three of the world's great religions began in the Mediterranean area—Judaism, Christianity, and Islam. "Jonah and the Great Fish" is an early Bible story. Another story, a silly one, from this part of the world is "Tales of the Hodja." This Hodja is a wise man who's not quite so clever as he thinks he is.

Spain is on the western, European side of the Mediterranean. Spanish culture is colorful and lively, as you'll see when you read "The Princess and the Pumpkin," a fairy tale from the Spanish island of Majorca.

From Egypt to Spain the Mediterranean is exciting and varied. Enjoy your trip!

50

# The Golden Touch

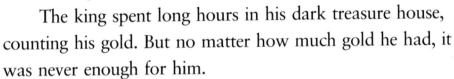

A GREEK MYTH

In the kingdom of Phrygia in Asia Minor there once lived a very rich king whose name was Midas. There were two things King Midas loved more than anything else in the world: his gold and his young daughter.

The king spent long hours in his dark treasure house, counting his gold. But no matter how much gold he had, it was never enough for him.

One day an old, weary traveler came to his palace, and Midas himself gave the man food and drink and a place to rest. Not long after, as Midas sat in his gloomy treasure house, a dazzling young man came through the narrow window, riding a sunbeam, and stood before him.

It was Bacchus, the god of the vine. The weary traveler had been Bacchus's teacher, and the god was grateful for Midas's kindness to his friend. Bacchus looked around the room and said, "What a wealthy man you must be, with so much gold."

"That is true," said the king, "but there is not so much gold here as there could be."

"What would satisfy you?" asked Bacchus. "Name the deepest wish of your heart, Midas, and it shall be granted."

Midas had often dreamed of what he would ask for if ever he had such a chance, and so at once he answered, "Oh, Bacchus, let everything I touch be turned to gold."

The god frowned. "You have chosen foolishly, Midas. Nevertheless, I have promised. At sunrise your wish will come true." Then Bacchus vanished.

The next morning Midas sprang out of bed, eager to test his power. First he touched his favorite book of poems, which lay on the table beside his bed. At once the words faded and the book turned to gold. Midas was startled at first and then thrilled.

As he put on his clothes, they too turned to gold. Wearing the heavy garments, Midas went out into his rose garden. As if in a trance he moved from bush to bush, changing each blossom and bud, leaf and branch to gold. As the color and fragrance of the living roses faded, a chill came over Midas. Hurriedly he went inside to eat breakfast.

As Midas picked up his knife to peel his orange, both knife and orange were changed to gold. When he bit into his bread, he got only a mouthful of golden crumbs. How on earth, he began to wonder, am I ever going to eat or drink anything?

Just then his little daughter came into the room, crying bitterly. In her hand she held one of the golden roses.

"What is the matter, dear child?" Midas asked. "Doesn't the wonderful rose please you?"

"It is not wonderful," sobbed the child. "It's cold and hard and has no sweet smell. It's ugly!"

Worried, King Midas stretched out his arm to comfort his daughter. But even as he touched her, she too hardened into gold. From the soles of her brown sandals to the curls of her brown hair, the child became a golden statue with golden tears on its cheeks.

Now Midas knew how wrong he had been. He cursed himself for his greed, wept for his child, and prayed that Bacchus would take away his unhappy gift.

Bacchus was merciful. He appeared once more in a shaft of sunlight and said, "You are wiser than you were, King Midas. Go now to the River Pactolus. Its water will

wash away the Golden Touch. A few drops of this water will restore the things you have turned to gold."

Midas bowed low, and when he looked up, Bacchus was gone. Midas hurried to the river and plunged in. He quenched his thirst with the pure water. Then he took up a clay pitcher that stood on the river bank. To his great relief, the pitcher remained clay. He filled it with water and ran to pour some on the golden statue that was his daughter. As life returned to her, joy returned to the king's heart. Together the two poured the life-giving water over the golden garden, and together they laughed as color and fragrance came back to the roses.

Thereafter, King Midas lived a simple life. He hated gold and loved only the gifts of the earth and the pleasures of human company. Only one thing remains to recall Midas's folly. To this day the sands of the River Pactolus glisten golden in the sun. And if you bend low over the river bank, you can hear the waters murmur:

Treasures lost and pleasures found,
Here the Golden Touch was drowned.

# Black Cloud from Vesuvius

## CHARNAN SIMON

## [ PART 1 ]

"Hurry up, Hercules!" Nonia impatiently tugged the rope around her donkey's neck. Although Hercules was small, he was strong, like the hero for whom he was named, and he didn't like to be rushed.

Nonia sighed. She and Hercules had spent a long morning delivering the fine cloth woven at her mother's loom. Now it was nearly lunchtime, and Nonia was hot and tired. They'd never get home at this rate, though, with Hercules stopping to nibble a leaf off every shrub along the way.

Nonia tried to soften her voice. "Come along, little Hercules," she coaxed. "There's a long drink of cool water waiting for you at home. Doesn't that sound good?"

Apparently it did, because after one last swish of his tail, the little donkey picked up his heels and trotted quickly down the street.

All around them, the citizens of the Roman seaside town of Herculaneum were also hurrying on their way. It was the twenty-fourth day of August, the last day of the Emperor Augustus's official birthday celebration, and the streets were more crowded than usual. People had gone to watch the athletic games in the huge palestra or to see the Greek and Roman plays in rehearsal at the theater. Now they were going home for lunch and a nap, or perhaps to the public baths, before the evening's celebrations began.

Nonia and Hercules had almost reached home when they came to the turnoff for Neapolis. Nonia tightened her grip on Hercules' rope. The donkey had come from that northern town last year, as a gift from Nonia's aunt, and he still thought the Neapolis road was the road home. Sure enough, when they came to the crossing, Hercules pricked up his ears.

"Oh, no you don't," said Nonia grimly. Bracing her feet, she gave a sharp tug on the rope. "*This* is your home now!"

It was a hot and dusty Nonia who finally reached the cool courtyard of her family's home nearly an hour later.

Her mother raised an eyebrow as Nonia came in.
"How far did you have to chase that animal this time?"
she asked.

"Just to the first olive grove," Nonia said, defending her
pet. "Really—he's beginning to know that this is his home."

Her father snorted. "I'd like to see the day that donkey
knows anything," he said. "Much more of this, and I'm
selling him to Lucius the baker. Lucius was telling me
just the other day that he needs a new donkey to turn his
mill wheels."

Nonia started to protest, but her mother shushed her.
"Your father is just teasing," she said. "Now eat your
lunch—fresh figs and melons, and your favorite cheese."

Hungrily, Nonia sat down to eat. Like most people in Herculaneum, her family took their summer meals in the open, airy courtyard in the center of their house. Here flowers grew brilliant in the southern sun, and water played cheerfully in the stone fountain.

When her father had finished his meal, he leaned back on his couch. "Nonia," he said, "I have some news for you."

Nonia looked up. "Good news?" she asked. It wasn't often that her father sounded so serious.

"Well, now, that depends," he replied.

"Oh, Marcus, stop teasing the child," her mother said, smiling at Nonia. "Of course it's good news."

Now her father was smiling too. "Do you remember the white woolen cloth you wove for your mother earlier this summer?"

Of course Nonia remembered. All her life she had wanted to be as fine a weaver as her mother. Justa's cloth was famous throughout Herculaneum, and the loom in her front workshop was seldom silent. Two years ago Justa had begun teaching Nonia to weave. Most of Nonia's cloth was used as polishing rags around the house. But finally she had produced three pieces of white woolen cloth that her mother had declared worthy of the family name.

Her father was speaking again. "I showed your cloth to Proconsul Balbus. He admired it and would like to buy it for his daughters. What do you think? Should I sell?"

Nonia could only stare at her father. Proconsul Balbus—one of the most important men in Herculaneum—wanted to buy her cloth!

"Oh, Father!" cried Nonia. "Is this true? How did it happen?"

Her father was about to answer when suddenly, without warning, a violent cracking sound split the air. The whole house heaved and shook. Thunderous roars seemed to come from the earth itself.

Nonia's father jumped to his feet. "Wait here!" he said sharply to Nonia and her mother. "I'll be right back!"

Nonia turned to her mother. "What is it?" she whispered, frightened. "Is the world ending?"

"No, no," her mother answered in a soothing voice. "You know how often the earth shakes here. This is just a bit worse than usual, that's all." She looked worried, however, as she spoke.

## [ PART 2 ]

By the time Nonia's father returned, the noise and the shaking had lessened. A fine flaking of ash was drifting into the courtyard, though, and a hot, sharp smell started to burn Nonia's nose and throat.

"It's Mount Vesuvius," her father said. "Something terrible has happened. Come—it's safe enough now to see for yourselves."

Once outside, Nonia gasped at what she saw. A huge black cloud, shaped like a tree, rose high into the sky above Mount Vesuvius. As the cloud spread, it dropped the fine ashen particles that Nonia was already brushing from her hair and eyes.

"What are we to do?" she asked nervously. "Will the mountain hurt us?"

Her mother and father exchanged a glance. "I think we'll stay where we are for now," her father said slowly. "There is a rumor that the Roman fleet across the bay at Misenum is setting sail. If that's true, and if the shaking continues, the boats will take us out of danger. But for the time being, I think we are safe enough at home."

And so they passed a restless afternoon and evening. It was a relief when bedtime finally came. Nonia had just fallen into a troubled sleep when she was awakened by her mother gently shaking her shoulder.

"Come, Nonia," she whispered. "We are going to the beach. The rumbling is getting worse, and the boats must be on their way by now."

The family was already on the street when Nonia stopped short. "My cloth!" she exclaimed. "I can't leave that behind!" And she darted back into the house before her parents could stop her. She picked up her precious packet of cloth from the workroom and then remembered something else. Quickly she slipped out the back door. When she rejoined her parents, she was leading Hercules.

Her father was furious. "Nonia! This is no time for running off! We could lose you in this crowd!"

It was true. The streets were jammed with people making their way to the harbor. All were hoping for some way to escape the increasingly thick cloud of ash and the now-greater rumbling of the earth beneath them.

When they reached the harbor, there was a stunned silence. The water was gone! Where once waves had lapped at the docks, there was now only sand on which all kinds of sea creatures were flopping about. Somehow the water had withdrawn from the beach and pulled itself back into the sea.

Her father didn't hesitate. "Come—we'll go back home. No boats will be coming this way, and we're safer inside with all this ash flying about."

Back they went, against the crowds of people still streaming toward the harbor. Now there was a sense of urgency in the air. Men were shouting and babies were crying as the rumbling grew wilder. It became harder and harder to breathe the ash-filled air.

"Nonia!" shouted her mother. "Your cloth—hold it over your mouth!"

For a moment Nonia hesitated. Her precious cloth—but her mother was right. The fine, tight weave would block the ash. She and her parents each took a piece and then pushed on.

They were just at the Neapolis crossroads when it happened. Hercules, already frightened by the crowds and the noise, pulled free from Nonia's hand. He didn't like this strange night. He was going home!

Without thinking, Nonia started after her pet. She was out of the walled gate and halfway up the Neapolis road by the time her parents caught up with her.

"Nonia!" said her father furiously, coughing and choking. "Didn't I tell you———"

Nonia's mother interrupted him. "Marcus!" she cried anxiously. "Look!"

They all turned around. The huge black cloud had spread out from Vesuvius and was now hanging over the city behind them. Bright, angry flames shot out of it. They could hear the screams of the townspeople in the distance. Then their city was completely blotted out.

Nonia and her parents stood for a moment, stunned. Then her father spoke slowly. "It seems your donkey knew best after all, Nonia. Such safety as there is tonight appears to lie toward Neapolis. Come, let's catch up with Hercules."

"But our friends!" Nonia cried. "Our home!"

Her mother laid a gentle hand on Nonia's shoulder. "Your father is right," she said sadly. "We cannot help anyone in Herculaneum now. But thanks to your stubborn donkey—and to your poor, ruined cloth—we can save ourselves. Now come."

On the road ahead Hercules brayed—a loud, impatient sound. Nonia took one last, heartbroken look at the only home she had ever known. Then she straightened her shoulders and turned toward Neapolis. Mount Vesuvius had spoken, and her life would never be the same again.

# Tales of the Hodja

### Retold by CHARLES DOWNING

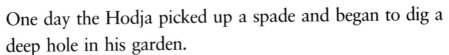

One day the Hodja picked up a spade and began to dig a deep hole in his garden.

His neighbor came up and asked him what he was doing.

"You and the others have been wondering for some time what to do with the earth that is lying at the side of the road after the repairs have been done to it. Well, I am digging a hole to bury it in."

"But Hodja," said the other, "where will you put the earth you are digging out of the hole?"

"Oh, come now!" said the Hodja. "I cannot attend to every detail."

The Hodja was once asked which was more useful, the sun or the moon.

"The sun shines in the daytime when there is a lot of light already," he replied, "whereas the moon shines when it is dark. The moon is therefore much more useful."

One day the Hodja dropped his ring inside the house. Not finding it there, he went outside and began to look around the doorway. His neighbor asked him what he was looking for.

"I have lost my ring," said the Hodja.

"Where did you lose it?" asked the neighbor.

"In my bedroom," said the Hodja.

"Why, then, are you looking for it out here?"

"There's more light out here," the Hodja replied.

One evening the Hodja was drawing water when he saw the reflection of the moon at the bottom of the well.

"The moon has fallen down my well," said the Hodja. "If I do not get it out, it will be the end of the world, and everyone will blame me!"

He tied a large iron hook to the end of a piece of rope and let it down the well. When he judged that he could hook the moon, he began to pull on the rope. The hook, however, had caught under a stone on the bottom of the well. The Hodja strained and pulled, until the hook suddenly dislodged the stone and flew up the well-shaft. The Hodja fell flat on his back.

"Allah be praised!" he said, seeing the moon in the sky. "It was a great effort, but I have got it back where it belongs!"

# Puddle Wonder

### MARGARET HILLERT

A puddle is a silver place
Where someone else's world begins.
I see the treetops made of lace.
The sky beneath me spreads and thins.
And I can see another face
All wavery and full of grins.

His world is upside down and dim.
I wonder how mine looks to him.

# Jonah and the Great Fish

Retold by WARWICK HUTTON

Long ago there lived a man called Jonah. One day he heard the voice of the Lord calling to him, and it said, "Arise and go to the city of Nineveh. The people there are wicked. You must preach and persuade them to give up their evil ways."

Jonah was frightened by the Lord's command. So he fled from the presence of the Lord, down to the port of Joppa. There, in the harbor, he found a ship that was about to sail to far-off Tarshish. He paid his fare and went on board, hoping to escape from the presence of the Lord.

The ship set sail, but almost at once the Lord sent out a great wind into the sea, and there was a mighty tempest. The wind and the waves grew ever more threatening. The sailors were afraid and they threw the cargo into the sea to lighten the ship.

All this time, Jonah, weary and worn, lay fast asleep. The captain woke him angrily. "Arise, O sleeper! Call upon your God to save us!"

The sailors believed that someone on board had brought bad luck to the ship. "Come and draw lots, so we may know who is causing this evil," they said. Jonah drew the black stick. Then they knew that he was the cause of their trouble.

So Jonah rose up and told them that he had feared the Lord's command and had fled from his presence.

The sailors were afraid. "What shall we do with you, Jonah, so that the sea will be calm again?" And Jonah answered, "Throw me into the sea. Only then will the waters be calm. I know that this great storm is upon us because of me."

Nevertheless, the sailors worked hard to bring the ship safely to land, but they could not. The sea was too rough and the winds were against them. They lost their oars and their sail.

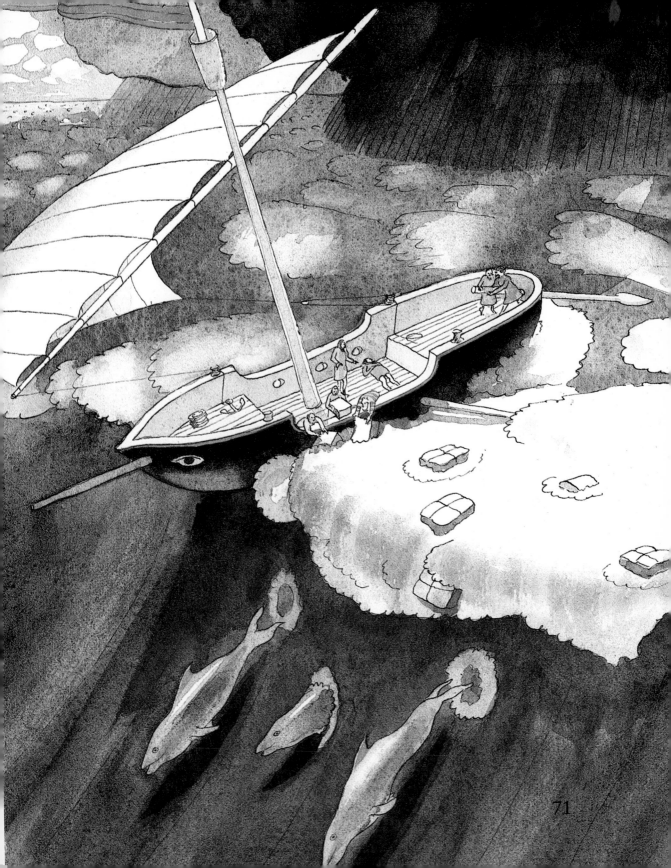

71

In despair, they begged Jonah to forgive them.
Then they lifted him up and threw him into the sea.

73

At once, the wind stopped raging, and the sea grew calm.

Now the Lord sent a great fish to swallow up Jonah.

And Jonah was in the belly of the fish for three days and three nights.

He prayed to the Lord from the great fish's belly, saying, "Lord, help me. You have cast me into the deep. Water stretches for miles around me. Vast waves roll over my head. I am banished from your sight. I will never again disobey your word, if only I can be saved, and from now on I will praise you and give thanks to you."

The Lord heard Jonah and spoke to the great fish. It vomited out Jonah upon the dry land.

Jonah went to Nineveh as the Lord had commanded. And the people of Nineveh gave up their evil ways and believed in the Lord.

# The Dead King

JUDY DONNELLY

Far away in the land of Egypt is a strange valley. It is lonely and silent. There are no trees and no grass or flowers—just jagged cliffs, rocks, and sand. It is called the Valley of the Kings, and it belongs to the dead. Thousands of years ago the kings of Egypt were buried there, along with fabulous treasures.

Many people hunted for the treasures. Howard Carter was one of them. He was an archeologist, a scientist who digs in the earth for clues about the past. He came to Egypt in 1890 when he was only 17 years old. He learned all about the ancient Egyptians and the Valley of the Kings.

Long, long ago, when an Egyptian king died, he was buried with his most prized belongings. Why? The kings believed that, after death, their spirits went to another world. To be happy there, a king's spirit would need everything the king loved in life: beautiful clothes, fine furniture, jewelry, even food. The spirit would need a body, too—a body that would last forever. So the Egyptians learned to wrap dead bodies to make them into mummies.

Because the kings wanted to be sure that their mummies and their treasures would be safe, many of them built giant pyramids. When they died, their mummies were sealed into these pyramids with all their treasures. But robbers broke into every one, so the kings decided to hide their burial places. They built secret tombs in the cliffs of the Valley of the Kings. They didn't know it, but their treasures still weren't safe.

For many years every archeologist who worked in Egypt dreamed of finding a king's tomb hidden in the valley. Almost 30 tombs were found. But ancient robbers had always been there first. The treasures were gone.

By 1900 most archeologists had decided that there were no more kings' tombs left to find. Howard Carter thought they were wrong. He was sure that one king's tomb had never been discovered. The king's name was Tutankhamen. Sometimes he was called King Tut. Tut wasn't an important king. He ruled for just a short time and died when he was only 18.

Carter met a man who agreed with him. He was a wealthy Englishman named Lord Carnarvon. The two became partners. Lord Carnarvon gave Carter all the money he needed for his search. In 1917 Carter began to dig in the valley.

For five long years Carter searched. He worked in burning heat, in terrible winds, and in blinding dust storms. He became tired and discouraged.

Lord Carnarvon wanted to give up, but Carter still had hope. He had dug up some stone huts built in ancient times. He had a feeling about them. He asked Lord Carnarvon for one more chance.

Carter and his workers began to dig under the first hut. They found one step cut into the rocky ground, then another and another. It was a hidden stairway! They cleared more rubble away. There was the top part of a door!

What was behind it? Could it be the entrance to a king's tomb? Carter felt like breaking down the door, but he remembered all the years Lord Carnarvon had helped him. He decided to wait for his friend to come from England.

Howard Carter and Lord Carnarvon at the entrance to Tut's tomb

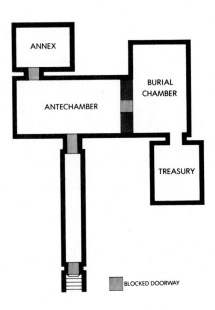

A diagram showing the rooms of Tut's tomb

Finally Lord Carnarvon arrived. Together he and Carter uncovered the bottom part of the door. They were amazed at what they saw. It was the royal seal of Tutankhamen. This was the king's tomb! At last Carter had found what he was looking for.

There was still one question. Would the tomb be empty?

They broke through the door. Behind it was a long passageway filled from floor to ceiling with small stones. It took many days to cart all the stones away. Then they came to another door.

Carter made a small hole in the door. His hands were shaking. He held up a candle. At first he couldn't see into the darkness. Then, slowly, he made out the shapes of statues and strange animals, and he saw gold. Gold everywhere! Lord Carnarvon was standing just behind him. "Can you see anything?" he asked. Carter could hardly speak. "Yes," he said. "Wonderful things!"

Carter made a larger opening in the door. Inside, the treasures seemed even more wonderful. He saw golden couches carved with strange animals, golden chariots, a chest full of jeweled robes and sandals, and a golden throne.

These treasures were all in one room. There were also three other rooms, all filled with treasures! King Tut's mummy rested in one of them. That was the rarest treasure.

The news of Carter's discovery spread around the world. Visitors poured into the valley. Strangers wrote to

Carter. Some of them warned him that he was in danger.
These people believed that there were evil spirits in the tomb.

Then, very suddenly, Lord Carnarvon died. Newspaper
reporters made up stories. They said he died because he had
gone into the tomb. They said there was a curse written on
King Tut's coffin and a deadly poison on the treasures. The
truth was that Lord Carnarvon's death had been caused
by an insect bite. He had been sick even before he came
to Egypt.

Carter missed his partner, but he wasn't afraid. He
went back to the tomb to open King Tut's coffin. He was
going to learn exactly how an Egyptian king was buried.

When he opened the coffin, he found another inside—and then another. The third coffin was made of solid gold, more than 200 pounds of it. Slowly Carter raised the lid. Inside was the mummy of the king. This was a special moment. Carter felt as though he were back in ancient Egypt, back in the time of Tut.

It took Carter 10 years to empty the tomb. There were more than 5,000 ancient treasures inside. Each one had to be treated with the greatest care. Carter kept a few of the treasures. The rest went to a museum in Egypt. King Tut's body was left where it had rested for over 3,000 years. It is still there today.

# Cats

ELEANOR FARJEON

Cats sleep
Anywhere,
Any table,
Any chair,
Top of piano,
Window-ledge,
In the middle,
On the edge,
Open drawer,
Empty shoe,
Anybody's
Lap will do,
Fitted in a
Cardboard box,
In the cupboard
With your frocks—
Anywhere!
*They* don't care!
Cats sleep
Anywhere.

# You've Come a Long Way, Kitty!

CAROLYN DUCKWORTH

Five thousand years ago, more or less, the African wildcat trotted into the lives of Egyptian farmers. It found plenty of rats and mice to eat among the grain the farmers stored. In return, the farmers allowed the African wildcat to live on their farms. As generations of wildcats grew up on the farms, they became more and more tame. After a thousand years or so, the Egyptian farm cats were no longer African wildcats. They had changed enough to become a different kind of cat—the domestic, or house, cat.

The Egyptians believed that the domestic cat was magical. Somehow, they thought, it made more grain grow. Its eyes seemed to tell the time of day, since the pupils narrowed at noon and widened at night. In fact, cats' pupils narrow during the day to keep out the sunlight. At night they open wide to let in as much light as possible. This is why cats can see so well in the dark.

a) Cats' eyes in light

b) Cats' eyes at night

The Egyptians also began to believe that the cat protected them during the night, which they feared so much.

For the next thousand years a cat-headed goddess named *Bastet* was one of Egypt's most important gods. Egyptians believed she protected grain and made fields fertile. They also thought she guarded their homes and kept their children healthy. To thank Bastet for her help, Egyptians protected all cats. Anyone who was caught killing a cat was killed. When a cat died,

Bastet

it was buried just as people were; some were even made into mummies. No cats were allowed to be taken out of the country.

Sailors from other countries heard about Egypt's "magic" cats. They began to steal the cats whenever they were in port. By 100 B.C., domestic cats were catching rats in Rome, Greece, and the Middle East. As Romans conquered the rest of Europe, cats traveled with them. Cats also went with merchants on their travels to Asia.

Cats were treated well the first thousand years they were outside of Egypt. From England to China, they earned their keep by killing rats and mice. Farmers continued to claim that cats made their fields more fertile. Many people believed they brought good luck. And some people still worshiped the cat as a god. But then cats ran into trouble in Europe.

About a thousand years ago, during the period of time we call the Middle Ages, many people in Europe began to believe that cats were evil creatures. They thought cats brought bad luck and were greedy and sneaky. Anyone who kept cats was thought to be a witch. These "witches" and their cats were often killed. For almost five hundred years cats were killed by the thousands just because people were afraid of them.

Fewer cats meant lots of rats. Some rats carried a deadly disease, the *bubonic plague,* or Black Death. But people didn't connect rats with the disease. All they knew was that there were far too many rats. Little by little people began to keep cats again to kill rats. By the 1700s cats were back on European farms and in cities, killing rats as they had for a thousand years before.

As cats became popular again in Europe, people began breeding them for certain colors and kinds of fur. They wanted newer and stranger kinds of cats. The French already had long-haired cats that had come from Asia. Then travelers found out that the Siamese people had been breeding a beautiful two-colored cat. When the first Siamese cats arrived in England, they became popular right away.

Cat breeding was a big business in Europe and the United States by 1900. Cat clubs were formed, and cat

Clockwise from the lower left:
Smokey Persian, Yellow Gaux, Calico, Tabby, Siamese

shows were held. People had gone cat crazy.

Today there seem to be as many cats as there are cat lovers. But no matter what their shape, size, color, or fur length, all domestic cats have one thing in common. They all came from those African wildcats that trotted onto Egyptian farms five thousand years ago.

# The Princess and the Pumpkin

A MAJORCAN FAIRY TALE
Adapted by MAGGIE DUFF

Long ago, in the island town of Palma, there lived a king
and queen who had a daughter. She was the prettiest thing
ever, with long golden hair, rosy cheeks, and eyes that
sparkled like the morning dew. Now this young and happy
princess loved to dance and sing, and the sound of her
laughter rang through the palace like thousands of tiny
silver bells.

One warm and sunny day, the princess was on her
balcony with her ladies-in-waiting. She played with her
kittens and sang gaily while the ladies combed her hair with
a golden comb. Suddenly—*swoosh!*—a flock of green birds
flew down from the sky. The leader seized
the golden comb in his beak, and—*swoosh!*—
the birds were gone again. The happy song
ceased and the princess grew silent.

The next day the princess returned to the balcony with her ladies-in-waiting. The ladies braided the princess's hair and were binding it with an emerald band when—*swoosh!*—the flock of green birds flew down from the sky. The leader seized the emerald band in his beak and—*swoosh!*—the birds were gone again. The happy smile faded from the princess's face.

The following day was cloudy and gray. The princess and her ladies-in-waiting sat on the balcony, wondering what to do on such a dark, gloomy day. Suddenly—*swoosh!*—the flock of green birds flew down from the sky. The leader snatched a strand of the princess's golden hair in his beak and—*swoosh!*—the birds were gone. Tears fell from the princess's eyes and splashed onto her hands.

After that, the princess took to her bed. She refused to eat or to be comforted, and as the days passed she became sadder and sadder and weaker and weaker. The most learned doctors and wisest people in the kingdom were called in, but they could not name the illness or find a cure.

At last they decided she must be under an evil spell and declared, "To break the spell and make her well, the princess must be made to laugh again!"

At once the king decreed that whoever in the kingdom could make the princess laugh, whether young or old, rich or poor, man or woman, would be kept in comfort forever.

The entire kingdom buzzed with the news. People came in droves to try to make the princess laugh, for they had nothing to lose and much to gain should they succeed. Some sang, some danced, and some came in costumes. Others told jokes and riddles and tried all sorts of tricks. Children stood on their heads and crossed their eyes while they wiggled their ears. Others came bringing horses dressed in skirts, dogs in bonnets, roosters in trousers, cats in carts, even donkeys wearing feathers. But alas and alack, not even a glimmer of a smile crossed the sad princess's face, and she grew still weaker.

Then one day when nearly all hope was gone and it was feared the princess would die, an old granny came to town. Now this old granny's back was bent, and her teeth were gone, but her eyes were bright and her step was light, and her tongue wagged on and on. When she heard the news about the princess and the royal decree, she decided right then and there that she would make the dying princess laugh. "For I would like to be kept in comfort the rest of my days," she told anyone who would listen.

The next morning the old granny was up early. She dressed in her Sunday best and set out for the palace. As she shuffled along—*tris tras, tris tras*—she tried to think of what she might say or do to make the princess laugh. But try as she would, nothing came to her head worth even a pig's ear.

"Oh dear," she sighed, "what if I should fail like the others? I would not like that at all!" Just then she spied an enormous pumpkin growing in a nearby field.

"Ah! What a pumpkin that is! I will pick it and carry it on my head to the palace. That should make the princess laugh!"

The old granny climbed the fence and walked over to the huge pumpkin. Taking hold of it with both hands, she pulled and pulled. But the pumpkin held fast. She pulled even harder. Suddenly the pumpkin broke loose and over she toppled.

She lay there moaning and groaning and calling for help, but none came. Finally she got up as best she could, dusted herself off, and made sure she had no broken bones. Then she looked around. Where the pumpkin had been, there was now a great, gaping hole! She crept to its side and cautiously peered down into it. The hole was so deep that she could not see the bottom. Then curiosity took hold and led her down into the hole.

When she finally came up she was chuckling gleefully, her aches and pains forgotten. She carefully covered the hole with sticks and grasses and slowly rolled the pumpkin back into place. Then she was off again for the palace—*trik, trek.*

When she arrived, the granny found the townspeople still milling about. "Am I too late?" she asked anxiously. "Does the fair princess still live?"

"The princess still lives," they answered.

"Has she laughed?" Granny asked.

"The princess will never laugh," said some.

"Ah then, make way for one who is here to make the princess laugh," called out the old granny as she pushed her way through the crowd.

When she finally reached the king and queen, they immediately took her to the princess.

The old granny bowed very low. "Ah, good day, my princess, star of my eyes and joy of my heart," she began. "Now you must believe, *señorita,* when I tell you that as soon as I heard of your strange illness, I came on foot as fast as I could from the far side of this island." The princess's eyelids fluttered. Then the granny's tongue wagged on and on as she told of finding the enormous pumpkin and how she had discovered the great gaping hole. "And what a bump I got, my princess, when I toppled over! But it will be well worth it if it makes the fair princess laugh." She paused.

The princess stirred, opened her eyes, and then said faintly, "Oh, Granny, tell on, do!"

The old granny told on. "Now, *señorita,* you must know and believe that when I went down into that hole I found many ladders with gold and silver rungs. I climbed down those ladders until I came to a room filled with tables laden with every good thing to eat you can possibly

imagine! I was so hungry, and it smelled so good that I
couldn't resist tasting something. As I reached out for a
pastry and a sweet, a terrible voice boomed out, 'Who
would take a pastry, and who would take a sweet?'

"'Just a good old granny who is very hungry,'
I answered.

"'A whack on the back and a jab in the ribs for that
old granny. This food is not for her!' the voice shouted.

"Then, my princess, a silver knife and a silver fork
jumped up from the table and started to whack me on the
back and jab me in the ribs. Oh, what a whacking and what

a jabbing! I can tell you, my princess, I would have been finished for sure if I had not scrambled out of there in a hurry. Then how could I have told you this tale?"

A smile played around the princess's lips, and her eyes began to dance as she spoke in a stronger voice. "Oh, Granny, do tell on!"

"I ran from that room," the granny continued, "and I came into a garden—the most beautiful ever! In the center, a fountain splashed and sparkled in the sun. I sat down to rest. Suddenly—*swoosh!*—down from the sky flew a flock of green birds. They flew right up to the fountain, and as the water splashed on them they turned into handsome young men. The leader was the most handsome of all, but he looked very sad. As he stood there, he took a golden box from his tunic. Reaching into it he held up in turn three glistening objects. Then sighing he said:

> This golden comb, this strand of hair,
> Emeralds the princess once did wear—
> How I wish I'd claimed her hand
> Before this spell fell on the land.
> Now she lies ill, and I have wings
> Until she laughs and claims these things . . .

"Just then a gust of wind came up, scattering water from the fountain. As it touched the young men, they turned into green birds and flew away.

"And then, *señorita*, my heart was lightened and I laughed with joy, my aches and pains forgotten, for I knew what I must do. I came as fast as I could to tell you this tale, and you must know and must believe, oh my princess, that every word I have spoken is as true as true can be!"

The princess sat up, her eyes sparkling. Her smile broke into laughter. She laughed and laughed until she was well and the roses returned to her cheeks.

"Well done, Granny, well done," the princess said merrily. "Now I must see everything just as you have told it. Let us go at once."

The ladies-in-waiting helped her get dressed while the king and queen danced for joy. A carriage was ordered, and off they drove.

When they arrived at the field they ran over to the huge pumpkin and carefully rolled it aside. Quickly they brushed the sticks and grasses away. Sure enough, there was the great, gaping hole. Then the granny and the princess hurried down the gold and silver ladders until they came to the room filled with tables. Sure enough, they were laden with good things to eat.

"Ah, my princess, do have a pastry and a sweet," coaxed the still-hungry granny.

When the princess reached out to take some, a voice called out angrily, "Who would take a pastry, and who would take a sweet?"

"The fair princess of Palma," the old granny answered.

"Let the princess take what she will. All is for her," said the voice.

The princess took a dainty bite of a piece of pastry, and then gave the rest to the old granny, who happily devoured it. Then the princess nibbled on a sweet and gave the rest to the granny, who quickly finished it too.

"Now, Granny, do lead on!" said the princess.

When they reached the garden, it was just as beautiful as the granny had said, and there in the center was the fountain, splashing and sparkling in the sun.

"Let us hide ourselves, my princess," the granny said, "and see what we will see."

Suddenly—*swoosh!*—out of the sky flew the flock of green birds. Right to the fountain they flew, and as the water splashed on them they turned into handsome young men. The leader took a golden box from his tunic. He

reached in and held up a golden comb. *Zas!*—a dainty hand darted out from the bushes, snatched the comb, and quickly disappeared.

The young man was startled. He reached into the golden box again and held up the emerald band. *Zas!*—a dainty hand darted out, snatched the band, and again disappeared.

The young man looked puzzled. He slowly reached into the box a third time. Carefully he wound the strand of golden hair around his finger before holding it up. *Zas!*—a dainty hand darted out to snatch the golden strand, but this time the handsome young man was ready. He caught the small hand and gently pulled until the beautiful princess came into view.

"Why did you take these treasures?" he asked wonderingly.

"Because they're mine!" the princess answered.

95

"Ah! Then you are my true love and have broken the wicked spell. We are free! Fair princess, will you marry me?"

"Gladly," she answered, for she liked what she saw, "providing my parents agree. You can ask now, for they await us at the top."

So with the granny leading the way, they climbed out of the hole. The prince, for that was what he was, fell to his knees before the king and queen and asked for the princess's hand in marriage. Quite overcome by all that had happened, they gave their consent at once. Then all returned to the palace, and the festivities began without delay. The wedding celebration lasted for days and days, with each day's entertainment better than the one before. And after that the prince and princess lived together happily for many years.

As for the old granny, true to the royal decree, she was kept in comfort for the rest of her days. Whenever foreign dignitaries came to court, she gladly told her story to anyone who would listen.

And now you must know and must believe that it's all as true as true can be!

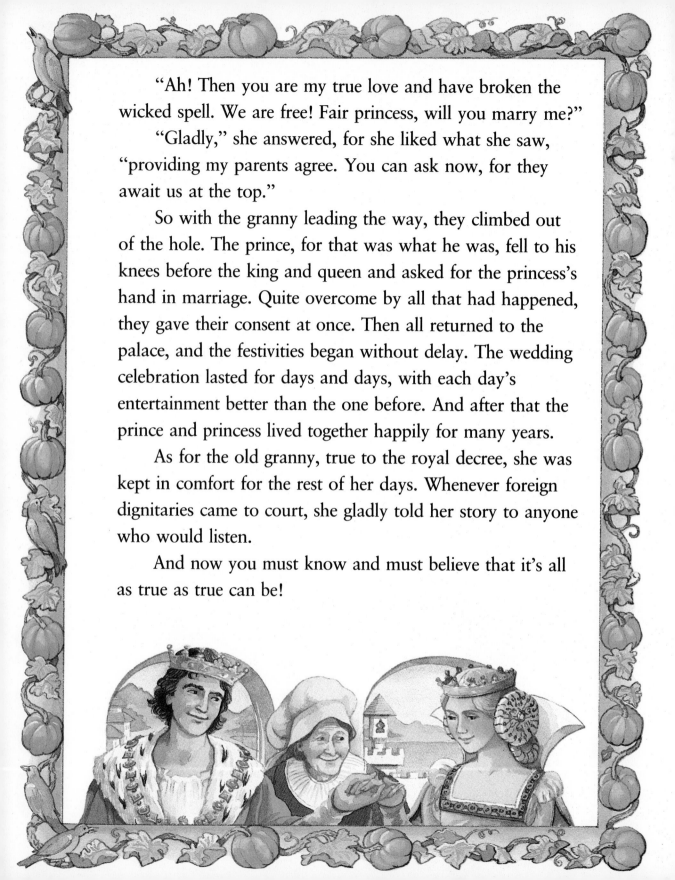

# Unit Three
## Africa

# Africa

Directly south of the Mediterranean Sea is the world's second-largest continent—Africa. Look at the map of Africa on page 99. The largest desert in the world, the Sahara, stretches across the northern third of the continent. The few people who live there are *nomads*, or people who move from place to place searching for food and water.

Africa has only a few small mountain ranges. Most of inland Africa is made up of high plains called *plateaus*. All around the coast of Africa, between the high plateaus and the sea, are much lower lands called *coastal lands*.

The rivers in Africa rage in thunderous waterfalls or race along as rapids. Very few of them can be traveled by boat. Because river travel was so difficult, little was known about the inner part of Africa for years. Only the people living there really knew what it was like.

Africa has much more land than Europe and far fewer people, yet there are parts of Africa that are crowded. Sections of Zaire, Ethiopia, and South Africa, for example, have far more people than the land can support.

Climate and soil are important resources in Africa. The food supply depends on them. In southwestern Africa, farmers must water their crops because there is never

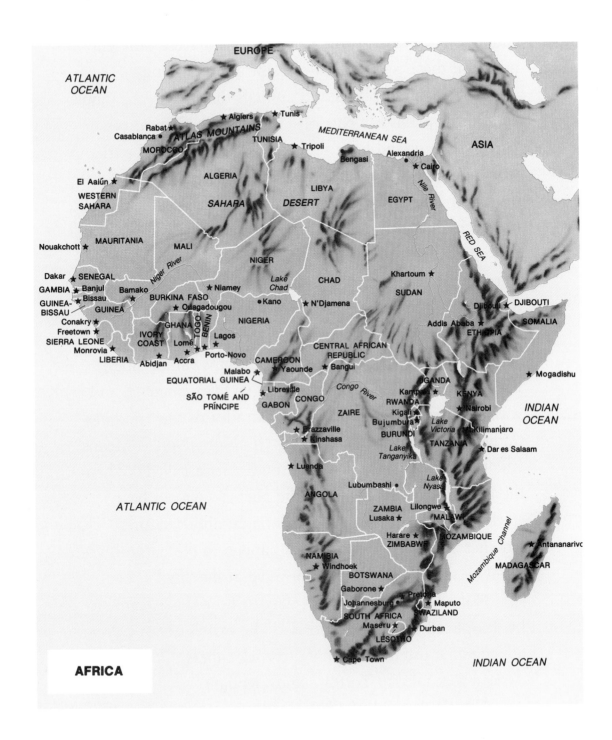

**AFRICA**

99

enough rain. People in the tropical areas have a different problem: there is too much rain for good farming.

The beautiful plants and animals that live in the jungles and on the plains are part of Africa's natural resources. Large areas of land have been set aside as national parks, where hunting is forbidden and the wild animals are protected. Every year thousands of tourists visit these parks to see chimpanzees, gorillas, elephants, giraffes, lions, rhinos, and other animals in their natural surroundings. You can learn about one of these animals in "Kifaru: The Black Rhino." And you can read about a family living in the largest national park in Kenya in "A Memorable Eclipse."

Millions of Africans belong to groups called tribes. Each of the thousands of tribes has its own language and way of doing things. You can get an idea of the "riddling" tradition in tribal life by reading "Ji-Nongo-Nongo Means Riddles." In the folk tale from South Africa called "When the Milky Way Happened to the Night" you can hear stories of how people long ago thought about nature. Another story about why things happen in the natural world is "Why the Sun and the Moon Live in the Sky."

Not all folk tales explain why or how things came to be. People all over the world also like stories about clever animals that use their cunning to trick others. One such African folk tale is "Tortoise and Elephant."

There's a world of adventure waiting for you in Africa!

# Ji-Nongo-Nongo Means Riddles

## VERNA AARDEMA

In the villages of Africa, among many different tribes, or groups of people, storytelling sessions include the sharing of riddles. Some riddles are very old and have been handed down from generation to generation. Many African riddles, like American riddles you may know, are just for fun. They are puzzling questions with funny or surprising answers. But many African riddles are actually proverbs in question form. They are wise sayings based on common sense, and they help you to see things in a new and simple way.

**Congo**

Who can trust his money to a monkey?
*The man who can climb trees.*

**Yoruba**

Who has a house too small for guests?
*The tortoise.*

**Ga**

What leaps down the mountain
but cannot climb back up?
*The mountain stream.*

### Ga

What is it that you look at with one
eye but never with two?
*The inside of a bottle.*

### Kanuri

What is it that even the ostrich
with its long neck and sharp
eyes cannot see?
*What will happen tomorrow.*

### Wolof

What kind of tree cannot shade you?
*One that is smaller than you are.*

### Hausa

What lies down when it's hungry and
stands up when it's full?
*A rice sack.*

### Masai

Who has more courage than a Masai warrior?
*Two Masai warriors.*

102

# When the Milky Way Happened to the Night

## A SOUTH AFRICAN FOLK TALE

Do you sometimes hear the sounds that a city makes? Do you hear it now? Kids are going at it fast this evening— playing ball, jumping rope, and running to tag a friend of theirs.

Do you hear it? A mother is calling for her boy to come in now. Listen. You can hear their footsteps on the sidewalk as they come running in to eat.

It is a quiet feeling you have now. Put your eyes to where the sun is hiding red behind the buildings. If we wait, soon the street lights will turn on. Above them, a black dome with stars like tiny eyes will be hanging over the neighborhood of our city.

Funny thoughts float inside my head when night comes on and people quiet down. If we took away the buildings, if we swept away the city, what would be left? Just we people and the wind and the sun and the stars.

Listen hard now, and you can hear the thoughts of the people in the beginning of things. Look close and look far—far away to a long ago time. Listen to people telling stories of how they saw life way back then in the early land of Africa. Hear their voices, if you have the ears and have the mind that can understand them. If you can, then South Africa speaks to you.

Look up now, if you dare, straight past the dark trees. Look up now into the black of night. The sky of the black night has a billion stars, which no one has counted because no one can. You see that lighted highway splashed against the wide black sky. What do you think? That white road is nothing but ashes spread wide up there—wood ashes and nothing else.

A long time ago, people had no stars at night. People then made fires on the ground to light up the dark.

One night, back in that time, a dreamy girl sat burning wood and keeping warm. Her fingers played with the cool white ashes. She smiled to see that when she tossed them up, the ashes would float against the night, with the flying sparks from her small blaze.

More wood she heaped on the fire. She stirred it up again and again to fly more sparks into the air, and great handfuls of ashes she scooped high into the night sky. Lovely they flew. Light they flew. High, high—up and up into the deep night sky.

So at this time, you can see them in the night—that girl's fire sparks—those waves of wood ashes from that girl's hand back then when night was black except for fires. Some call it the Starry Road. Some say the Milky Way. But *we* know: they are a dreamy girl's sparks and wood ashes that put brightness into the night.

# A Memorable Eclipse

CHRISTINA E. KIOKO

Kip stretched and turned over on his side. Carefully he pulled the mosquito net from under the mattress and snaked his hand up to lift the curtain from the window. The dawn sky was cloudless above the ragged hills and plains of the Kenya landscape.

Letting the curtain drop, Kip rolled over and nudged his younger brother, Peter, who was still sleeping beside him.

"Peter, wake up. The sky is clear—it's going to be a beautiful day!" He couldn't keep the excitement from his voice. Peter's eyes popped open, but he didn't move.

"Peter, don't you remember?" whispered Kip. "Today is the eclipse!"

Suddenly Peter remembered. He sat up quickly and smiled at his brother.

"Let's go and let out the *kukus*," Kip said, loosening the mosquito net at the bottom of the mattress.

The two boys scrambled out of bed, ran down the hall, and dashed out the open front door, stopping on the long veranda. They always had to stop and look before rushing into the yard in the early morning because the buffaloes that often grazed on the sprinkled grass were very dangerous if startled.

There were no buffaloes today, so the boys ran around the side of the veranda and flung open the door of the chicken house. A rooster and three hens came hurtling down, flapping their wings as they chased each other noisily to the birdbath.

Kip and Peter walked back to the house. Mother met them at the front door. "You boys get dressed," she said. "We'll have breakfast here on the veranda. And hurry—there's a lot to do before the eclipse starts."

Kip and Peter passed their father in the hallway. "Hi, boys," he said. "Are you ready for the big day?"

"Where are you going, Baba?" asked Peter. Their father was a game warden in charge of the largest national park in Kenya.

"I want to fly around to check on all the people who have come to see the eclipse. The gate at Voi had to stay open two extra hours last night to let all of them into the park. I don't know whether there was enough space for everyone at the campsites."

By the time the boys had dressed and were back on the veranda, their father's small plane was taxiing down the airstrip at the bottom of the hill on which their house stood.

"Here, boys, you can sit on the steps," Mother said, handing them each a mug of warm cornmeal porridge and a piece of toast. As they sat there eating, Kip thought about the people who had come from all over the world to watch the eclipse. He and his family were lucky to be able to see the whole thing from their own front yard.

After breakfast Mother got out a thermometer and put it on the veranda wall.

"Kip, you'll be in charge of reading the thermometer. Write down the temperature every fifteen minutes to see how far it drops during the eclipse."

Kip looked at his watch and at the thermometer. Then he wrote *9:30—92°* on a piece of paper.

Mother then brought out a piece of paper that looked like smooth tin foil.

"This is a special filter we can look through to watch the eclipse. If you look at the sun directly, its rays are strengthened by the lens in your eye, and the retina in the back of your eye can be badly burned. This paper filters out harmful rays."

They went out on the lawn and took turns looking at the sun through the filter. Kip thought it was like magic. You could look right at the sun. It really was a bright, fiery ball.

Later Mother brought out a large cardboard carton that had no cover.

"Come on, boys," she said, "let's make that pinhole viewer I was telling you about." She put a piece of white paper inside the box on the narrow side. On the opposite side she poked a hole using a small nail.

Kip and Peter watched through the open top as she placed the carton so the side with the hole faced the sun. The small hole focused a bright image of the sun onto the paper.

"Hey, look! The sun isn't round any more," shouted Kip. Sure enough, the moon was beginning to move across the sun.

Kip ran to the porch, checked the thermometer, and wrote *10:15—91°*on his paper. Then he rushed back to the box to see the lopsided image again. When Peter handed him the filter paper, he could clearly see the dark shape of the moon beginning to hide the sun.

Slowly, over the next hour, Kip and Peter watched the sun shrink and felt the temperature drop. It now seemed like a cloudy day and then like dusk.

"The eclipse should be total soon, Peter," Kip said at 11:20. "Baba's just going to make it." There was almost nothing left of the sun's image in the box, and the temperature was down to 74° when their father came back up the hill from the airstrip.

A few minutes later, the sharp edge of the moon's shadow raced across the lawn. As Kip looked through the

filter paper, the last rays of the disappearing sun shone through a deep lunar valley, making a brilliant splash of light at one spot of the moon's silhouette.

"Look, Peter," he said excitedly, handing the filter to his brother. "It looks just like a diamond ring—what a sparkle!"

But by then the moon had completely blocked the sun's rays, and they no longer needed the special filter to watch the eclipse. The sky was a deep, dark blue, and the atmosphere was cool and hushed.

"A halo," said Peter, pointing to the shimmering streamers of light surrounding the moon's black disk.

"It does look like a halo," agreed their father. "That's called the *corona*, Peter. This is it, boys—the eclipse is total!"

"Wow," said Kip. "I can see stars out! In the middle of the day!"

Mother laughed. "Those two bright 'stars' outshining the others are the planets Venus and Mercury," she said. "You can only see Mercury during a solar eclipse—usually its orbit keeps it too close to the sun for the human eye to see."

The family stood in silence for a moment. There was an eerie twilight—there were no shadows, and colors were

111

dimmed. Kip looked out over the plains that stretched below their house. Nearby, they were darkened by the moon's shadow. Farther away they appeared bright, though Kip knew they were still only lit by half-light.

Everything was motionless and quiet. Even the birds that usually filled their garden with color and song were still, waiting for the sun to return. It was a magic moment. Kip shivered.

Then he remembered his job. "It's 11:25," he said, checking his watch, "and the temperature is 68°."

After about five minutes, the other edge of the moon's shadow passed across the lawn as the moon continued moving eastward. The birds began to sing. Light gradually returned to the yard as Kip and Peter watched the sun's image appear again in their pinhole viewer. Slowly the image grew. The show was over.

# Kifaru: The Black Rhino

FRED JOHNSON

Have you ever watched a scene on television or in the movies in which a giant rhinoceros charges a jeep and batters it into tin cans?

This kind of scene is very exciting but gives the black rhino a bad reputation that it really doesn't deserve. What the film doesn't tell you is that the dreaded black rhino charge is, more often than not, just a lot of bluff and noise.

Some Africans call the black rhinoceros *Kifaru,* which means "Stupid One" in their language. Kifaru isn't stupid,

but the animal can't help seeming so to us because it is so near-sighted that it is almost blind. Still, the English name for Kifaru is no more accurate than the African name. The black rhino is not black; it is gray.

The Africans have an old story they tell about Kifaru. The story says that long ago animals had no fur or hides, so they were given needles to sew their coats together. Kifaru dropped his needle, and in pawing and peering around to find it, he kicked it under a bush. He had to sew his coat together with a thorn, and it came out very baggy. Then he decided that someone had stolen his needle. To this day he charges things—still trying to find the thief who took his needle.

Since the rhino can't see very well, its world is one of sounds and smells. Kifaru's hearing and sense of smell are keen. If a twig snaps or a rodent scoots off in the grass, Kifaru notices at once and may become alarmed. Often the animal panics and flees, snorting and thumping away. Or it may advance like a runaway dump truck. This is the beginning of the "dreaded" charge of the black rhino.

An alarmed black rhino is likely to charge anything it hears or smells. It may charge cars, trucks, trees, bushes, campfires, people, rodents, toads, or rustling leaves. Kifaru can do a great deal of damage to whatever it charges.

Still, the rhino often misses its target. Because it sees so poorly, it has only a fuzzy view of what is all around. Its small eyes are on the sides of its head. To see anything up ahead, the rhino must twist its great head from side to side to let one eye or the other peer ahead.

When a rhino finally decides that it has something lined up, it charges. It snorts and kicks up a lot of dust, which makes the great animal appear even more frightening. Sometimes it stops short after running only a few feet. The rhino may keep on with its charge, though, and at the last minute lower its head, point its horns forward, and run blindly. Generally the rhino misses its target by as much as ten feet (three meters). Sometimes this is because the nearly blind creature has not been able to aim itself at its target. Sometimes, though, the rhino does not mean to complete its charge. It is merely bluffing, trying to scare away whatever has startled it.

The black rhino can run as fast as twenty-eight miles (forty-five kilometers) an hour. It walks and runs on one toe—the wide middle one that presses against the ground and bears the animal's great weight. The two smaller toes at the side seem to be of little use.

At birth, black rhinos weigh about fifty pounds (twenty-two kilograms) and stand about twenty inches

(fifty centimeters) tall. About an hour after birth the baby is standing on its stubby legs. It staggers about, sniffing and listening to a world it can barely see.

The baby stays close to mother rhino for two to four years. At first it nurses often. Then the growing animal eats more and more of the food the mother eats. By the time the rhino is fully grown, at five years, it may weigh two thousand pounds (950 kilograms), be 12.5 feet (3.75 meters) long, and stand 5 feet (1.5 meters) tall at the shoulder.

Rhinos seem to have metal-lined stomachs. Leaves of a certain tree have a sap that will seriously blister the skin of a human being, but the black rhino munches them with

enjoyment. The sap of another tree is used by some Africans to poison arrow tips—with which to kill rhinos. In Kifaru's bloodstream the sap can do its deadly work. But in the rhino's stomach it is just part of dinner. The rhino crunches up, swallows, and digests heavy thorns as if they were crackers.

Like many African hoofed animals, the black rhino feeds mostly in the cool of the early morning and early evening. Between feeding times rhinos flop down in the dust and snooze. About the only thing that can wake one is the ear-splitting noise that the tick birds make when something gets too close. These birds feast continually on the ticks that live on the rhino's thick hide. They make a big racket that warns the rhino that something is coming. Then Kifaru struggles up and prepares for the famous rhino charge—or, more likely, rushes off in panic.

Adult rhinos have only one enemy—human beings. For centuries some people have believed that rhino horn can be used to make a powerful medicine. When powdered and taken in a drink, it is supposed to make people become more youthful. The black rhino has two horns, which it uses when it charges. The front one can grow to be more than $3\frac{1}{2}$ feet (1 meter) long. The horns are not bony like a cow's; instead, they are like tightly matted hair. But none of this makes rhino horn a good medicine. It doesn't work as a medicine at all. Nevertheless, poachers continue to kill rhinos illegally just to get the horns. The rest of the animal is left to rot or to be eaten by vultures and other scavengers.

Some people are in daily touch with black rhinos in animal reserves and zoos. They say that once the animal learns to trust a human being, it seems to want to make friends. It will follow a person around the way a pet dog might. Imagine Kifaru wanting to be your friend!

# The Rhinoceros

OGDEN NASH

The rhino is a homely beast,
For human eyes he's not a feast,
But you and I will never know
Why nature chose to make him so.
Farewell, farewell, you old rhinoceros,
I'll stare at something less prepoceros.

# Sizes

JOHN CIARDI

If you were as big as a giant flea,
How much would you have to grow to be
The size of the tiniest head-to-tail
Very most midgety baby whale?

I mean to say—and it's no surprise—
Whatever you do about your size,
There's always something a size or two
Very much bigger or smaller than you.

I mean to say, what's big of some
Is small of others. Now get along home.
And whether you stay or wander far,
Be just the size of whatever you are.

119

# Tortoise and Elephant

AN EAST AFRICAN TALE
Retold by RUTH MANNING-SANDERS

Tortoise was walking along a path through the forest when she met Elephant.

Elephant said, "Tortoise, get out of my way, or I shall step on you."

Tortoise was offended. She said, "What! *You* step on *me*?"

Elephant said, "Certainly!"

Tortoise said, "You couldn't step on me. I'd jump over your head."

Elephant said, "You can't jump one inch."

Tortoise said, "I *can* jump! I *can* jump!"

Elephant said, "Well, let's see you."

Tortoise said, "No, I'm not going to jump today. I've come a long way, and I'm tired."

Elephant said, "Ha, ha, boaster! Now you're looking for excuses!"

Tortoise said, "No, I am *not* looking for excuses. Tomorrow let us meet here again. Then you'll see whether I can jump or not!"

Elephant said, "All right," and he walked off.

Next day Tortoise brought her sister to the meeting place. They were as alike as two peas in a pod. She hid her sister under the bushes on one side of the path and stood on the other side of the path herself. Then along came Elephant. He didn't know there were two tortoises, one on either side of him. He could see only one.

"Oh, there you are, Tortoise!"

"Yes, here I am."

"Well, are you going to jump?"

"Of course I'm going to jump."

"What! Over my head?"

"Yes, over your head."

"Well, let's see you!"

"Stand still then," said Tortoise. "Don't you move."

"I *am* standing still," said Elephant. "Go on, jump!"

Tortoise made a little run. "Hupp!" cried she.

121

"Hey!" cried Tortoise's sister, coming out from under the bushes on the other side of Elephant.

Elephant swung around. Could he believe his eyes? Yes, there was Tortoise on the other side of him!

"Thousand thunders!" said Elephant. "Do it again, Tortoise!"

"Stand still then," said Tortoise's sister.

Elephant stood still.

Tortoise's sister made a little run. "Hupp!" cried she.

"Hey!" cried Tortoise on the other side of Elephant.

Elephant swung around. Thousand thunders! There was Tortoise!

"So you see I *can* jump," said Tortoise.

"Well, I have to admit that," said Elephant. "Right over my back! I couldn't jump so high myself."

Then Elephant went slowly home. He was hanging his head.

Tortoise and her sister laughed and laughed. They danced around, and Tortoise played on her flute: *fing-fing-fing-kulo-fong-fing!*

122

# Why the Sun and the Moon Live in the Sky

NIGERIAN FOLK TALE
ELPHINSTONE DAYRELL

Many years ago the sun and water were great friends, and both lived on the earth together. The sun very often used to visit the water, but the water never returned his visits. At last the sun asked the water why he never came to his house. The water replied that the sun's house was not big enough and that if he came with his people he would drive the sun out.

124

The water then said, "If you wish me to visit you, you must build a very large house. I warn you, though, that it will have to be a very large place, as my people are very numerous and take up a lot of room."

The sun promised to build a very large house. Soon afterwards he returned to his wife, the moon, who greeted him with a broad smile.

The sun told the moon what he had promised the water, and the next day he began building a large house in which to entertain his friend. When it was completed, he asked the water to come to visit him.

When the water arrived, one of his people called out to the sun and asked whether it would be safe for the water to enter. The sun answered, "Yes, tell my friend to come in."

The water then began to flow in, accompanied by the fish and all the water animals. Very soon the water was knee-deep, so he asked the sun if it was still safe. The sun again said, "Yes," so more of them came in.

When the water was level with the top of a man's head, the water said to the sun, "Do you want more of my people to come?"

127

The sun and the moon both answered, "Yes," not knowing any better. So the water's people flowed on, until the sun and the moon had to perch themselves on top of the roof.

Again the water asked the sun the same question. He received the same answer, so more of his people rushed in.

The water very soon overflowed the top of the roof. Then the sun and moon were forced to go up into the sky, where they have remained ever since.

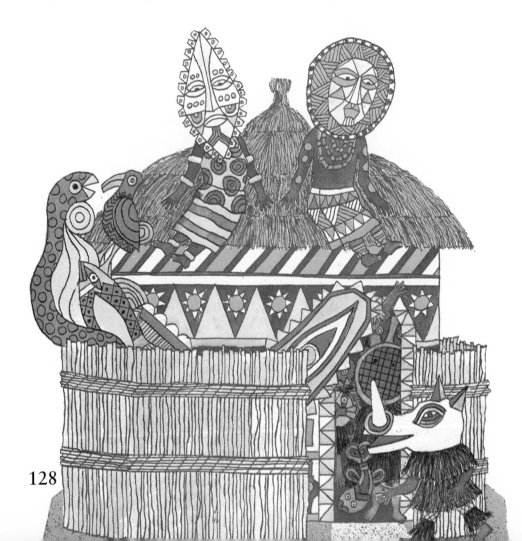

# Unit Four
## Asia and the Pacific

# Asia and the Pacific

Next we will visit the continents of Asia and Australia. One is the largest continent in the world, and the other is the smallest. Look at the map and find these two continents.

Asia is the largest continent in the world and has the most people. The people of Asia, like those on other continents, come from many different backgrounds. They have different religions and speak different languages. In crowded Asia, very little land is wasted. Farmers grow crops on even the smallest plots of land.

Asia is full of amazing sights and stories. In "The Great Wall of China" you'll learn about the only man-made structure on earth that can be seen from outer space. In "Imo's Discovery" you'll read about a clever monkey named Imo, who lived on the Japanese island of Koshima.

Modern Asian cities like Tokyo, in Japan, are very similar to modern American cities. Some everyday habits and traditions are still very different, however, as you'll discover in "Some Days We Eat with Chopsticks." The Japanese are also famous for a kind of poetry called *haiku*. Each haiku is only three lines and seventeen syllables long, yet it describes its subject so vividly that the reader can almost see, hear, feel, taste, or smell it!

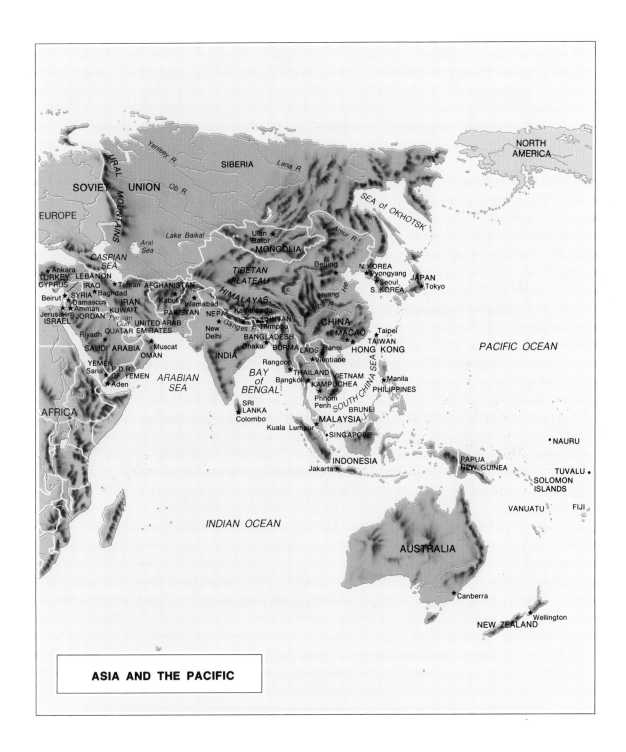

NORTH
AMERICA

SIBERIA
Yenisey R.
Lena R.
Ob R.
SOVIET UNION
EUROPE
SEA of OKHOTSK
URAL MOUNTAINS
Lake Baikal
Aral Sea
Ulan ★ Bator
MONGOLIA
Amur R.
CASPIAN SEA
Ankara ★
TURKEY LEBANON
CYPRUS IRAQ
Beirut ★ SYRIA ★ Baghdad
Damascus
Amman
Jerusalem JORDAN
ISRAEL
★ Tehran AFGHANISTAN
IRAN
Kabul ★
Islamabad
PAKISTAN
KUWAIT
QUATAR
UNITED ARAB
EMIRATES
Persian Gulf
TIBETAN PLATEAU
Beijing ★
N. KOREA
★ Pyongyang
★ Seoul
S. KOREA
JAPAN
★ Tokyo
Huang He
HIMALAYAS
Kathmandu
NEPAL ★ BHUTAN
Thimphu ★
CHINA
MACAO ★
★ Taipei
TAIWAN
HONG KONG
PACIFIC OCEAN
Riyadh ★
SAUDI ARABIA
MUSCAT
OMAN
YEMEN
Sana P.D.R.
★ OF YEMEN
Aden
New Delhi ★
Ganges R.
BANGLADESH
Dhaka ★
INDIA
BURMA
Rangoon ★
BAY of BENGAL
ARABIAN SEA
LAOS Hanoi ★
★ Vientiane
THAILAND VIETNAM
Bangkok ★ KAMPUCHEA
Phnom Penh
Manila ★
PHILIPPINES
SOUTH CHINA SEA
AFRICA
SRI LANKA
Colombo ★
Kuala Lumpur
BRUNEI
MALAYSIA
★ SINGAPORE
• NAURU
INDONESIA
Jakarta ★
PAPUA NEW GUINEA
TUVALU •
SOLOMON ISLANDS
VANUATU
FIJI
INDIAN OCEAN
AUSTRALIA
★ Canberra
NEW ZEALAND
Wellington

**ASIA AND THE PACIFIC**

From India comes a fable about six wise men who can't seem to agree on what an elephant looks like and a traditional riddle just begging to be answered. From the Philippine Islands comes another fantasy explanation about the natural world like those you read from Africa. In this tale you'll discover "How the Firefly Got Its Light."

Look at the map again. If you were to sail south into the Pacific Ocean from Asia, you would soon reach the island of Australia, the smallest continent in the world. It is often called the country "down under." The center of Australia is desert. It is called the outback or the bush, and few people live there. Most Australians live along the coast.

Many of the Aborigines, the first people to live in Australia, still live in the outback. You can read about their way of life and the unusual tool they have created in "The Stick That Comes When You Call It." In Australia you can find animals that are found nowhere else in the world—the platypus, the kangaroo, the wombat, and the koala.

If you sail east from Australia in the South Pacific Ocean, you come up to the small island of Tahiti. This is where a famous French painter, Paul Gauguin, lived and worked for many years. In "The Art of Paul Gauguin" you will learn from his paintings how Gauguin saw Tahiti.

Scientists think that a land bridge once connected Asia and Australia. After the bridge disappeared, the plants, animals, people, and cultures developed very differently, as you will see from these stories.

# The Blind Men and the Elephant

## AN INDIAN FABLE

Many years ago there were six wise men living in the country called India. Though all six were blind, they were known far and wide for their great learning.

One fine day the six blind men were talking among themselves. "We have often heard about this beast called the elephant," said one. "But we have never agreed on what it is really like. Let us find such an animal. Then we can feel it and see who is right and who is wrong."

"Fine," said the other blind men, and they went to the river where the elephant drank.

The first blind man walked up to the elephant. He placed his hand on the animal's broad back. "It is as I thought," he said. "The elephant is very much like a wall."

The second blind man happened to touch the elephant's tusk. He felt the smooth, sharp surface and shook his head. "Oh, no, you are wrong. The elephant is just like a spear!"

The third blind man was very short. His hand fell on the elephant's thick leg. "You are both wrong," he said. "The elephant is like the trunk of a tree."

The fourth blind man grabbed hold of the elephant's trunk. He felt it twisting in his hands and stepped back quickly. "None of you has studied the elephant carefully enough. It is clear that it is like a huge snake."

The fifth blind man stepped forward. He was slapped gently in the face by one of the elephant's waving ears. He carefully felt the ear with his fingers. "What can you all be thinking?" he asked. "This elephant is in every way just like a large fan. Can you not feel the breeze it stirs up?"

The sixth blind man was standing behind the elephant. When he reached out, he took hold of the animal's tail. "All of you are mistaken," he announced. "Surely you can tell that the elephant is like a swinging rope."

And so the blind men still could not agree on what the elephant was like. Each of them was partly right, and all of them were wrong. So they quarreled more than ever.

# Who?

INDIAN RIDDLE

Who whistled at my window?
Who stroked and smoothed my gown?
Who brought the scent of flowers?
Who knocked their petals down?

Who shook the yellow mango?
Who dropped it from its tree?
Who rattled all the branches?
Who tried to hide from me?

*(The wind)*

135

# Three Haiku

Please bird, don't go yet.
You are the finishing touch
To the snowy branch.

*Kazue Mizumura*

Again and again.
The wind wipes away the clouds
And shines up the moon.

*Kazue Mizumura*

Beautiful picture
Wet green grass painted by rain
Shining sun returns

*Ryoko Yuta*

# The Great Wall of China

## LEONARD EVERETT FISHER

About twenty-two hundred years ago, King Cheng of Ch'in
conquered the kingdoms of Han, Sung, Yen, Yüeh, Ch'i,
Chou, Chao, Ch'u, Wei, Wey Wu, and Lu. Tiny Ch'in
became a huge empire: China. And King Cheng became
Ch'in Shih Huang Ti, the First Supreme Emperor of China.

China was difficult to manage. Each of the old
kingdoms had its own system of weights, measures, money,

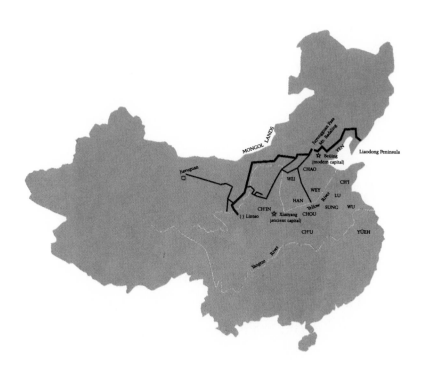

and writing. A grain of rice in Chao did not weigh the same in Chou. A hat size in Han was not the same in Sung. Money earned in Ch'i could not be spent in Ch'u. And officials in Wu could not read reports from officials in Lu. But the emperor brought order to his unwieldy lands. He made the systems of weights, measures, money, and writing the same everywhere. He even made everyone wear the same color: black.

Bringing order to his empire was not Ch'in Shih Huang Ti's only problem. In the north, fierce Mongol horsemen raided Chinese villages. They attacked the people and stole their goods. The Mongols threatened to invade all of China. Ch'in Shih Huang Ti rose in anger. "I must stop these barbarians!" he roared at the royal advisors.

"They are cruel," warned Li Ssu, the Prime Minister.

"They are tricky," added Chao Kao, Minister of the Household.

"And they are strong," declared Grand General Meng Tian.

"Soon they will fall on us," wailed the emperor's oldest son and Keeper of the Seals. "What will become of us? How shall we save ourselves?"

"With a wall!" Ch'in Shih Huang Ti bellowed.

"A wall? What wall?" the royal advisors asked. "We have many walls. None of them can stop these barbarians."

"I shall fix the old walls," replied the emperor. "I shall build a new and mightier wall and shall join all the walls together. I shall have one long wall across the top of China. It will stretch from Liaodong in the east to Lintao in the west. It will be six horses wide at the top, eight at the bottom, and five men high. I shall build it at the edge of our steepest mountains. No Mongol barbarian will be able to go around it, over it, under it, or through it. It will be the Great Wall!"

Ch'in Shih Huang Ti ordered Grand General Meng Tian to make preparations. The general's soldiers grabbed criminals, cheats, troublemakers, and anyone the emperor did not like. They dragged humble people from their homes. They forced musicians, teachers, writers, and artists to join the army of workers.

"And take that whining son of mine, Fu Su," the emperor commanded.

When all was ready, Grand General Meng Tian mounted his horse. With a wave of his arm, seven hundred thousand workers and three hundred thousand soldiers—one million people—marched north to build Ch'in Shih Huang Ti's Great Wall.

Tens of thousands of people were put to work fixing the old walls. Thousands more were made to pound the earth into thick, high mounds and to shape the mounds with bamboo poles.

Mobs of workers made huge, heavy bricks from clay. They cut large, square stones as well. These they fitted to

the sides and tops of the earthen mounds. The entire wall, from one end of Ch'in Shih Huang Ti's China to the other, they faced with brick and stone.

Every one hundred yards, the workers built watchtowers two stories high. Now the Mongols could be seen coming. Warning signals could be sent. There would be no more surprise attacks.

The Mongols watched from distant hills. They were unable to attack so many workers and soldiers on the high slopes.

No one was allowed to rest. "You, there!" screamed the soldiers, cracking their whips. "Faster! Faster! Work! Work! No idlers here!"

The Chinese worked day and night. Workers who complained or who ran away were caught and buried alive. Many workers lived out their lives building the wall. Many were buried in the wall.

The wall grew slowly, winding up and down the mountains. Roadways at the top were paved with three layers of brick. They connected the watchtowers. They were wide enough to hold ten soldiers side by side.

Finally, after ten years of labor, the wall was finished. Ch'in Shih Huang Ti came to inspect his Great Wall. He was overjoyed. "I have stopped the Mongols," he shouted. "We are saved at last. Forever."

Ch'in Shih Huang Ti was right. The Great Wall was so strong that the Mongols did not threaten China again for more than a thousand years. Later, other emperors improved Ch'in Shih Huang Ti's Great Wall. The last improvements were made by the Ming emperors between A.D. 1368 and 1644. Today the Great Wall creeps across the north of China like a wounded dragon. Sections of the 3750 miles of wall lie in ruin. However, the People's Republic of China is restoring parts of the Great Wall. The wall will remain a testament to China's long history, her strength, and the constant toil of her people.

# Who Am I?

FELICE HOLMAN

The trees ask me,
And the sky,
And the sea asks me
 *Who am I?*

The grass asks me,
And the sand,
And the rocks ask me
 *Who I am.*

The wind tells me
At nightfall,
And the rain tells me
 *Someone small.*

Someone small
Someone small
*But a piece*
 *of*
 *it*
 *all.*

# Some Days We Eat with Chopsticks

INA R. FRIEDMAN

In our house, some days we eat with chopsticks and some days we eat with knives and forks. For me, it's natural.

When my mother met my father, she was a Japanese schoolgirl and he was an American sailor. His ship was stationed in Yokohama.

Every day my father, whose name is John, walked in the park with my mother, Aiko. They sat on a bench and talked. But my father was afraid to invite my mother to dinner.

If we go to a restaurant, he thought, I'll go hungry because I don't know how to eat with chopsticks. And if I go hungry, I'll act like a bear. Then Aiko won't like me. I'd better not ask her to dinner.

My mother wondered why my father never invited her to dinner. Perhaps John is afraid I don't know how to eat with a knife and fork and I'll look silly, she thought. Maybe it is best if he doesn't invite me to dinner.

So they walked and talked and never ate a bowl of rice or a piece of bread together.

One day, the captain of my father's ship said, "John, in three weeks the ship is leaving Japan."

My father was sad. He wanted to marry my mother. How can I ask her to marry me? he thought. I don't even know if we like the same food. And if we don't, we'll go hungry. It's hard to be happy if you're hungry. I'll have to find out what food she likes. And I'll have to learn to eat with chopsticks.

So he went to a Japanese restaurant.

Everyone sat on cushions around low tables. My father bowed to the waiter. "Please, teach me to eat with chopsticks."

"Of course," said the waiter, bowing.

The waiter brought a bowl of rice and a plate of sukiyaki. Sukiyaki is made of small pieces of vegetables, meat, and tofu. It smelled good. My father wanted to gobble it up.

The waiter placed two chopsticks between my father's fingers. "Hold the bottom chopstick still. Move the top one to pick up the food," the waiter said.

My father tried, but the meat slipped off his chopsticks and fell on his lap.

The waiter came back with a bowl of soup. How can I eat soup with chopsticks? my father thought.

"Drink," said the waiter. "Drink from the bowl."

"Thank goodness," my father said. After the soup my father felt better. He picked up the chopsticks. Finally, my father put one piece of meat in his mouth. Delicious!

"More soup, please," he said.

After three bowls of soup my father felt much better. Then he practiced some more with his chopsticks. Soon, there was more sukiyaki in his belly than on the floor. But it was too late to call my mother. He had to run back to his ship.

That night my mother was sad. Every other day my father had come to see her. That day he did not come. He did not call on the telephone. Perhaps he was tired of walking and talking. Perhaps he was ashamed of her because she did not know how to eat with a knife and fork. Perhaps his ship had sailed away. All night she could not sleep.

And all night my father sat on his bunk, pretending to pick up sukiyaki.

The next morning my father called my mother. "Please, will you eat dinner with me tonight?"

"Yes!" my mother shouted into the phone. First she was happy. Then she was afraid. She took her schoolbooks and ran to the house of Great Uncle.

Great Uncle had visited England. He had seen the British Museum. He had eaten dinners with Englishmen.

My mother knocked at the door. Great Uncle opened it.

147

"Why are you so sad, child?" he asked.

"Because I must learn to eat with a knife and fork by seven o'clock tonight."

Great Uncle nodded. "Foreign ways are quite strange. Why do you want to eat with a knife and fork?"

My mother blushed.

"Is it the American sailor?" Great Uncle asked. "I see . . . Here, take this note to your teacher. At lunchtime I will come and take you to a foreign restaurant. By seven o'clock tonight you will eat with a knife and fork."

My mother picked up her school bag and bowed.

"No," Great Uncle stuck out his hand. "In the West you shake hands."

The restaurant had red carpets and many lights. Great Uncle pulled out a chair for my mother. "In the West men help ladies into chairs," he told her.

My mother looked at the small fork and the large fork on the left. She looked at the knife, little spoon, and big spoon on the right. Her head grew dizzy.

"Different utensils for different foods," Great Uncle said.

"How strange to dirty so many things," said my mother. "A chopstick is a chopstick. I can eat everything with two chopsticks."

When the waiter brought the soup, Great Uncle pointed at the large spoon. "Dip it slowly, bring it to your mouth. Sip quietly."

148

My mother's hand trembled. The soup spilled onto the white cloth.

"You'll learn," Great Uncle encouraged her.

When my mother was finished with the soup, the waiter brought her a plate of mashed potatoes, roast beef, and peas.

"This is the way Westerners eat," Great Uncle said. "With the knife and fork they cut the meat. Then they hold the fork upside down in their left hand. Like birds, they build a nest of mashed potatoes. They put the peas in the nest with the knife. Then they slip the nest into their mouth. Try it."

The mashed potatoes were not difficult. But the peas rolled all over the plate. "Impossible," said my mother. "I'll never learn by seven o'clock tonight."

"You can learn anything," Great Uncle said. "Try again. More mashed potatoes and peas, please," he said to the waiter.

At seven o'clock my father came to see my mother. "Why didn't you wear your kimono?" he asked. "We are going to a Japanese restaurant."

"A Japanese restaurant? Don't you think I know how to eat Western food?" my mother asked.

"Of course. Don't you think I know how to eat Japanese food?"

"Of course."

"Then, tonight we'll eat meat and potatoes. Tomorrow night we'll eat sukiyaki."

"Tomorrow night I will wear my kimono," my mother said. She started to bow. Then she stopped and put out her hand. My father shook it.

My father ordered two plates of mashed potatoes, roast beef, and peas. He watched my mother cut the meat into pieces. He stared when she turned over her fork and made a bird's nest. He was amazed.

"You are very clever with a knife and fork," he said.

"Thank you," said my mother.

"You must teach me," my father said. "That's a new way of eating peas."

"Teach you?"

"Yes, Americans don't eat that way." He slid his fork under some peas and put them in his mouth.

My mother stared at him. "But Great Uncle taught me. He lived in England. He knows the ways of the West."

My father began to laugh. "He taught you to eat like an Englishman. Americans eat differently."

"Oh, dear," my mother said. "A chopstick is a chopstick. Everyone uses them in the same way."

"Yes. When we are married we'll eat only with chopsticks." He took her hand.

"Married! If I marry you, I want to eat like an American."

"I'll teach you to eat with a knife and fork, and you teach me to use chopsticks."

My mother shook my father's hand. My father bowed.

That's why, at our house, some days we eat with chopsticks, and some days we eat with knives and forks.

# Imo's Discovery

## SHEILAGH S. OGILVIE

This is a true story about a small band of monkeys that lived on the little Japanese island of Koshima. These were very clever monkeys called *macaques*.

The macaques lived in the thick forest on the mountain slopes of Koshima. During the summer and fall they ate fruit and leaves. In the winter they searched about under the bare trees for twigs and bits of bark to eat. They never went down to the sandy beach and the blue sea at all.

Then one day, scientists came to Koshima to study the way the macaques lived. A small island is a good place to study animals because they can never go very far away.

The scientists wanted the monkeys to come out of the woods and into the open, where they would be easier to watch, so they began to leave pieces of sweet potato on the beach. At first the monkeys were too shy to leave the trees. Then, after a while, they began to slip out onto the beach just long enough to grab a slice of sweet potato and eat it. When they saw that the scientists didn't hurt them or do anything to frighten them, they stopped being shy.

One of the monkeys was a young female the scientists called Imo. Imo was unusually clever and curious, even for a macaque. One day, when she was just a year and a half old, Imo did something new, something no monkey on Koshima had ever done before. She picked up a piece of sweet potato from the beach. But she didn't toss it into her mouth, sand and all, as she usually did.

Instead, Imo took the sweet potato to the edge of the stream that ran into the sea. She dunked it into the water. With her free hand, she brushed the sand off it. Then she

ate it. Clean sweet potato tasted good. From that day on, Imo washed every piece of sweet potato she ate.

Imo's playmates saw what she was doing. A month later, another young monkey was rinsing her sweet potato in just the same way. Four months after that, Imo's mother began to wash her potato pieces too.

One monkey learned from another. Within five years, fifteen of the nineteen young monkeys were rinsing their potatoes. Two of the five grown-up females had learned to do so too. Only the adult males kept on eating sand with their sweet potatoes. They ate apart from the other macaques and probably didn't see what was going on.

Three years after Imo's discovery, the monkeys were still coming to the beach every day, but they were eating up the sweet potatoes very quickly. The scientists wanted the monkeys to stay out in the open for a longer time, so they began to sprinkle grains of wheat along the beach. Sometimes they even stamped it into the sand. The monkeys spent hours each day picking the grains of wheat out of the sand.

At least they did until the day that Imo scooped up a handful of wheat and sand and tossed it into the water. The sand fell to the bottom, but the wheat grains floated on top. Imo swept the wheat up into her mouth. She had just discovered a way to get plenty of wheat with very little effort.

154

The other macaques were quick to catch on to a good thing. Soon all the monkeys in the band were washing their wheat.

Imo lived for a long time. She is dead now, but her band of macaques still lives on Koshima. They have learned to play in the sea—some of them can even swim. They all wash their sweet potatoes and rinse their wheat. Their lives have changed since they came out of the trees.

# The Art of Paul Gauguin

ADELINE PETER and ERNEST RABOFF

Paul Gauguin was born in Paris on 7 June 1848. His father, Clovis Gauguin, was a journalist. His mother, Aline, was the daughter of a famous writer.

After his father's death Paul and his mother spent four years in Lima, Peru. At the age of seven he returned to France to begin his schooling. Later, he spent several years as a sailor. Then he went to work in a Paris bank.

In 1873, at the age of twenty-five, Paul married Mette Gad, who was Danish. They had five children in the next ten years. During this same time he became friendly with artists and began to paint.

In 1883, Gauguin lost his job and was forced to move his family to Denmark. Determined to become a professional painter, he returned to Paris alone. There he studied different styles of art and finally developed his own style.

Seeking a simple, natural way of life, Gauguin moved to the islands of the South Pacific. His paintings are beautiful studies of the landscape and the peaceful ways of the people.

In *Tahitian Landscape* our eyes sweep from golden foreground to towering red mountain. What a feeling of

*Tahitian Landscape*   Minneapolis Institute of Arts, Minneapolis

peace and harmony Gauguin has created with his sunlit meadows, colorful trees, bright shrubs, and soaring mountain!

As we look along the two broad, pink footpaths at the bottom of the landscape, we see a man wearing a straw hat. He is balancing two bunches of fruit on his carrying pole. Beyond him we follow the green shrubs to the black dog at the left. We pass the layered tropical growths and are reminded of how tall the graceful palm trees are and how high the mountain rises.

The painting is filled with the bright and exotic colors of Tahiti. The colors are chosen and combined in a way unique to Gauguin. We recognize his painting as both real and fanciful.

The artist painted this scene just five months after his arrival in Tahiti. He wrote home to France: "I feel all of this penetrating me and now can rest in extraordinary fashion."

*Ta Matete* means "The Marketplace." The busy and colorful marketplace was always outdoors. It was close to the water, which was very important to the people's lives. The marketplace of each village was not only the place where people shopped but also the center of their social life.

The women could wear their prettiest dresses and enjoy a few hours with friends away from their family chores. How pleasant to shop or to sit beneath the shady trees, to talk with friends near cool green grass, to watch the men

158

*Ta Matete (THE MARKET)*   Kunstmuseum, Basel

carrying in their fresh fish on long poles, to relax by the rushing sea and enjoy all the activity.

The artist painted these beautiful women almost the same way the Egyptian princesses were painted in Egypt's very old pyramids.

Paul Gauguin loved the simple way of life he found on the islands of the South Pacific Ocean. In all of his paintings there is a calm, a peace, that shows the contentment he found in his work. His paintings tell us that doing work we love brings us happiness.

*Girl with Mango*   Baltimore Museum of Art

# Until I Saw the Sea

LILIAN MOORE

Until I saw the sea
I did not know
that wind
could wrinkle water so.

I never knew
that sun
could splinter a whole sea of blue.

Nor
did I know before,
a sea breathes in and out
upon a shore.

# How the Firefly Got Its Light

## A FILIPINO TALE

A long, long time ago, the King of the Air lost his special ring. Now the king was proud of that ring, and he wanted to get it back again. So he called the animals together and asked them to help look for his ring. As a prize, the animal that found the ring could name any wish in the world, and the King of the Air would grant it.

You can imagine what a hustle and bustle there was as all the animals began hunting. Only a small beetle sat still and did not search for the ring. The King of the Air noticed this, so he asked the beetle, "Why do you not hunt for my ring, little beetle? Have you no wish you would like granted?"

The beetle answered, "Indeed, I do have a wish, Your Highness, but there is no need to search for the ring. From where I sit I can see it shining as it hangs on one of the points of your golden crown."

Then the King of the Air took off his crown, and there indeed he found the ring hanging from one of the points. The king was so pleased that he said to the little beetle, "Choose your own reward, and it shall be granted you."

"Your Highness," answered the beetle, "all day my family and I work hard. When night comes, we would like to play. But then the sun is gone, and it is too dark in the forest. Let the sun shine upon us all the time."

"That is a wish I cannot grant," the king answered. "The sun too must have its rest. But this I will do for you. I will give to you and to each of your family a tiny lantern that you may carry with you at all times, and when night comes it will light your way."

So the beetle took the lantern. It is not lighted in the daytime, but at night it glows brightly. That is why, ever since that day, the small beetle and its family have been called fireflies.

163

# The Stick That Comes When You Call It

CHARNAN SIMON

In some ways the country of Australia is the opposite of the United States. When it is morning here, it is nighttime there. When we are having summer, the Australians are having winter. And when you throw a stick in Australia, as often as not the stick comes sailing right back to you!

What is this surprising stick that comes when you call it? It's the boomerang!

A boomerang is a flat, curved piece of wood that really does return to the thrower after it is thrown. It was first used by the Aborigine people of Australia thousands of years

ago. The Aborigines were nomads. As they moved about the central Australian desert looking for food and shelter, they could only carry a few things with them. Everything they carried had to be very useful. The boomerang was an important tool. It was used for hunting, for starting fires, and for cutting and scraping. Boomerang-throwing contests were a popular sport. Boomerangs were often used as rhythm instruments and sometimes traded for other things the people needed. Some boomerangs were beautifully decorated with carved or painted designs. These designs often showed Australian wildlife, like the kangaroo or the koala or the wombat. Some told stories about Aborigine legends and traditions.

There are actually two kinds of boomerangs, the returning boomerang and the nonreturning boomerang. Both kinds are made from pieces of green wood that have been heated and then bent in the middle. The boomerang's curved shape makes it spin when it is thrown correctly. This spin makes the boomerang hit its target with more force than an ordinary rock or stick.

A returning, a decorative, and a nonreturning boomerang used for hunting

A returning boomerang is designed so that its spin and unbalanced weight make it turn in the air after it is thrown. An expert thrower can make a returning boomerang fly as high as fifty feet and turn several circles in the air on its way back. A really expert thrower doesn't have to move an inch to catch the boomerang when it returns.

Aborigines still use the returning boomerang to hunt birds and in contests to see who can make the best throw. The nonreturning boomerang, however, is a dangerous weapon, and it is never used for sport. It is larger and heavier than the returning boomerang, and it can be thrown with more accuracy. The best hunters can hurl this boomerang as far as 150 feet to stun and kill wild game.

Today, many Aborigines have left the desert and moved to Australia's coastal cities. Many of their traditions have changed, and they don't need boomerangs to survive in the city. Modern boomerangs are made in factories and sold as toys or souvenirs. People all over the world are fascinated by the way these simple curved sticks come back when they are thrown. You may even have one of your own!

But in some places in Australia's outback, the old ways of life still exist. Aborigines still carve and decorate their boomerangs in the ancient patterns. Whether used to hunt food in the desert by day or to clap along with songs and chants by the fireside at night, boomerangs are still a vital part of Aborigine life.

# Unit Five
## The Americas

# The Americas

Our imaginary trip ends back home in the Americas, on the continents of North and South America. When you look at your map, you can see that the Americas stretch almost from the North Pole to the South Pole, from the Arctic Ocean to Antarctica. The long neck of land that is Central America joins North America to South America. If you drove day and night at a steady fifty-five miles per hour, without stopping even once, it would take seven days to get from northern Alaska to the tip of Argentina.

Find the United States on your map. Together with Canada, Mexico, Central America, and most of the Caribbean Islands, it makes up the continent of North America.

The people of North America speak several languages. We in the United States speak English, as do the Canadians. Many Canadians also speak French, as do some of the people in the Caribbean. That is because England and France once ruled much of North America. Most of the rest of the people in North America speak Spanish. The people of South America speak Spanish or Portuguese, because Spain and Portugal once ruled much of that continent.

Many people in the Americas also speak different Indian languages. Indians were the first Americans, and there are hundreds of different Indian groups living in North and South America. For many centuries, Indians were the only people living here. Then people began to come from other continents—from Europe, Africa, and Asia. Today the Americas are home to people of many different races and cultures—a more mixed group than on any other continent.

Some of the stories you are about to read are about children not so very different from yourself. "Ramona's Book Report" could be about any third-grade girl in any classroom in the United States—any girl with a sense of humor, that is! In "The Pudding Like a Night on the Sea," two boys help their father prepare a special surprise for their mother—and learn something about responsibility and cooperation in the bargain.

Families all over the world like to help each other. Josefina February lives on the Caribbean island of Haiti in a one-room house with bamboo walls and a banana leaf roof. She doesn't have much money—but she knows how to earn a special present for her grandfather. Pablito also lives on a Caribbean island, in the city of San Juan in Puerto Rico. In "The Musical Palm Tree" you can follow Pablito around his lovely and historic city, as he combines hard work and lots of imagination to come up with a very special gift for his mother's birthday!

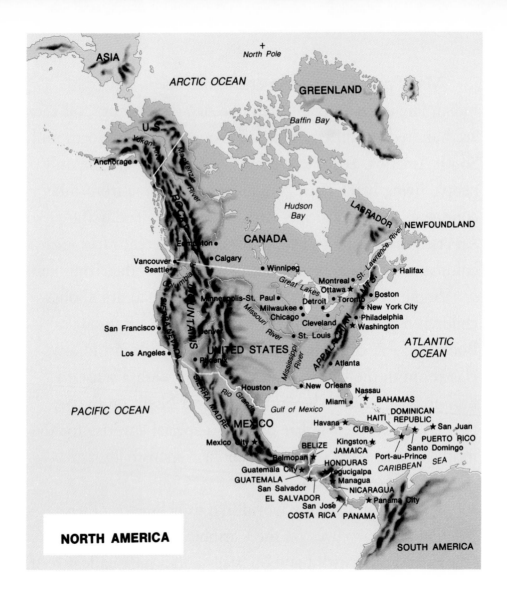

**NORTH AMERICA**

Moving north, you will enjoy a folk tale from Mexico about three sons who try to do a truly noble deed. Then, from *really* far north, comes another real-life story, this time about a girl who lives in Manitoba, Canada. When she looks out her front window, she sees polar bears on parade!

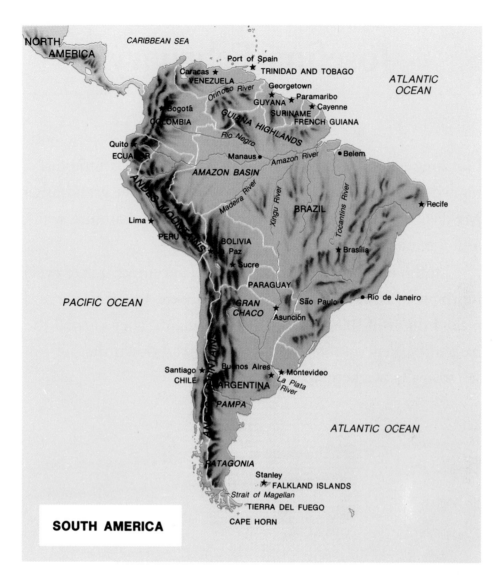

SOUTH AMERICA

After you have finished reading the stories in this unit, you will have completed your trip around the world. Think about what you have learned. How are the people you have met alike? How are they different? What have you learned about the things we share that make us all part of the same world?

# Josefina February

EVALINE NESS

Not long ago on a high hill in Haiti there lived a little girl named Josefina February. Josefina lived with her grandfather, Mr. February, in a house that had one room, bamboo walls, and a banana-leaf roof.

In the back of their house was a fruit grove. Early every morning Josefina and her grandfather went to the grove and picked the fruit that had ripened overnight. They carried the fruit in baskets on their heads and walked down the hill to sell it in the marketplace.

One morning, instead of going to market, Mr. February went to work all day in Mr. Hippolyte's sugar-cane fields. He told Josefina to play at home—but Josefina had other plans.

That day was her grandfather's birthday, and Josefina wanted to buy him a pair of real leather shoes. She decided to go to the market alone. If she could sell one basket of fruit she would have enough money to buy the shoes.

After her grandfather left, Josefina took her basket and went to the grove. While she was gathering the oranges, mangoes, bananas, and yams, she heard a strange sound. Josefina looked up and saw a little black burro, with a fringe of brown hair on top of his head that looked like a cap. His legs were so wobbly he could hardly stand, and his ears looked as long as his legs.

Josefina picked him up and held him close. The little burro folded his soft ears and put his head under Josefina's chin. She decided to call him Cap.

She wondered if Cap belonged to someone. How she wished he belonged to her! She would teach him clever tricks.

She would play games with him. And when he was older, she would ride on his back to the sea.

Josefina was so busy dreaming of the future, it was noon before she remembered the fruit she had picked to take to the market. She couldn't bear the thought of leaving Cap, so she decided to take him with her.

As she stood there in the noonday sun, Josefina suddenly felt cold. What if Cap belonged to the very first person she met? Would that be worse than the very last? First, last, last or first, it would be the same. If Cap belonged to someone else, he couldn't belong to her.

But perhaps he was like Josefina, who had no mother, no father, no sister, no brother. Cap might not even have a grandfather. He might, just possibly, belong to no one in the whole world except Josefina!

Somehow she felt warmer, so she put her basket on her head, picked up Cap, and started down the hill.

The first person she met was Lilly, the tallest, haughtiest girl on the hill. Lilly had a bandanna full of bananas on her head. "Pardon me, Lilly," Josefina said. "As you can see, I have a baby burro here. Does he belong to you?"

Lilly swept by without a word.

When Lilly had gone, Josefina whispered to Cap, "Well, anyway, it wasn't the *first* person."

She met no one else until she reached the bottom of

174

the hill. There she saw a little girl and her brother selling oranges by the roadside. Josefina went up to them and said, "Pardon me. As you can see, I have a baby burro here. What do you think of him?"

The girl and her brother, as if they were one, said, "We wish he belonged to us!"

Josefina smiled and continued along the road. Suddenly she heard a croak, a cackle, and a screech. She turned around and saw an old woman with three blackbirds. When Josefina asked, "Pardon me, have you lost a baby burro?" the old woman said not a word, but the three blackbirds cackled and croaked, "Not we, not we, not we!"

Josefina hugged Cap and hurried on to the market-place. When she got there she could hardly believe her eyes.

The marketplace was empty! All the people had taken their wares and gone home to supper.

Josefina didn't know what to do. She was happy and sad at the same time. Now Cap belonged to her. But she had not sold the fruit, and she had no real leather shoes to give to her grandfather for his birthday.

She started to walk slowly home. As she passed Mr. Hippolyte's sugar-cane fields, she was surprised to hear her name called. It was Mr. Hippolyte himself, leaning on the fence with his big straw hat resting on his nose.

Josefina tried to smile, but instead she started to cry. She cried so hard she thought she would never be able to stop long enough to tell Mr. Hippolyte her terrible trouble. Mr. Hippolyte just waited. At last Josefina wiped away her tears and told him her story.

Mr. Hippolyte looked at Josefina a long time. Then he said, "It just happens that I have a new pair of real leather shoes. Would you consider trading Cap for the shoes?"

It was Josefina's turn to look at Mr. Hippolyte a long time. Then she nodded her head. She was afraid to speak for fear she would cry again.

While she waited for Mr. Hippolyte to return with the shoes, Josefina did cry a little more. She made two neat braids in Cap's mane and tied them with the ribbons from her hair. She kissed Cap's nose and told him to be good. She promised Cap she would never, never forget him.

176

When Josefina got home, it was almost dark. She cooked ham and yams in a big pot and cut up all the fruit from her basket for dessert. She had just put the shoes in the middle of the table when Mr. February walked in. He stood there and smiled at Josefina. And Josefina stood there and smiled back. Then Mr. February put on his real leather shoes and kissed Josefina on top of her head.

Mr. February and Josefina ate the birthday supper in silence. They had almost finished when Mr. February said, "Poor Mr. Hippolyte. He has a responsibility, not a very big one, but he thinks he cannot handle it alone. He wondered if you would like to take care of it for him."

Josefina stared at her grandfather. Mr. Hippolyte had a responsibility! She started to speak, but before she could say a word the door slowly opened.

And in wobbled a little black burro, fringed on top, with ribbons in his mane.

# Polar Bear

### WILLIAM JAY SMITH

The Polar Bear never makes his bed;
He sleeps on a cake of ice instead.
He has no blanket, no quilt, no sheet
Except the rain and snow and sleet.
He drifts about on a white ice floe
While cold winds howl and blizzards blow
And the temperature drops to forty below.
The Polar Bear never makes his bed;
The blanket he pulls up over his head
Is lined with soft and feathery snow.
If ever he rose and turned on the light,
He would find a world of bathtub white,
And icebergs floating through the night.

# When the Bears Come to Town

PAM COATES

Polar bears visit my yard just as squirrels or raccoons may visit yours. This happens during October and November, when the weather starts to get cold.

I didn't know much about polar bears until I moved to Churchill, in Manitoba, Canada, a year ago. Of course, I had seen polar bears in zoos. I knew they were big, and I liked their white fur and their big, floppy feet.

It didn't take long for us to hear about the polar bears here in Churchill. Everyone said they would be coming to town . . . soon. We began reading about them as soon as school started.

We learned that Manitoba polar bears spend the summers pretty much living off their own body fat. Some of them roam the tundra eating berries and birds' eggs and

small animals. All of them are very hungry by the time
fall comes.

Churchill is very near Hudson Bay. The bears come to
the bay to hunt for seals, their favorite food, but they can't
start hunting until the water of the bay freezes. So some of
them wander around Churchill, finding food wherever—and
however—they can.

It seemed strange to me that the bears can't hunt until
the ice forms. Mrs. Finch, our teacher, told us it's because of
the way the bears hunt. A polar bear finds a hole in the ice
where a seal comes up to breathe. Then it waits and waits
for the seal to appear. The bear strikes like lightning, grabs
the seal with its claws, and hauls it up onto the ice.

A polar bear can also stalk its prey. Its fur blends into
the snowy background so well that the seal or bird it is
hunting usually doesn't see the bear.

When the "bear time" in
Churchill started, we were
warned to stay off the streets,
especially at night. We took
the bus to school. When we
wanted to have fun after
school, we took the city bus
to a big building called the
Complex. It has a sports
arena, a library, a theater,

and space for all kinds of activities. I felt safe inside the Complex. But bears are often seen nearby because it is the building closest to the bay. This is where I saw my first wild polar bear.

The bear was walking right toward the Complex. I couldn't believe how big it was. I told my friends, Beth and Al, to look out the window. Then we ran to tell the nearest guard. By the time we got back, the bear was already gone.

One reason the bears come so close to Churchill is that their keen sense of smell tells them there is food in garbage cans and at the dump. A bear can rip apart a garbage can with its strong paws and claws.

Some bears keep coming back to town and getting into trouble. First they have to be caught in giant, can-like traps. Then they are *tranquilized*, or quieted down, with a drug and airlifted by helicopter to big holding pens. The bears are kept caged until the ice freezes. Then they are set free.

Scientists study these polar bears while they are still in the pens. Collars with electronic beepers are put on the bears before they are let go. The beepers tell scientists where the bears travel. Once in a while a real problem bear has to

be shot. It happens only when the bear is a threat to
someone's life.

After hearing so much and learning so much about
polar bears, I really wanted to *see* more bears. But I was
afraid of getting hurt. The rule here in Churchill is "The
only good polar bear is a *distant* polar bear." Then our
next-door neighbor, Ted, offered to take my family out in
his big pickup truck. He would take us to a place where we
might see the bears yet still be safe.

We saw our first bear walking toward the city dump.

Its feet were kicking up lots of snow. This bear was even bigger than the one I had seen before.

"Wow," said Ted. "He's as big as a Volkswagen!" I was glad we were in such a heavy truck. Ted said that some polar bears are so strong they can turn over a small car.

As we got closer to the city dump, we saw some young bears. One was drinking out of a soda pop bottle.

When we drove farther out of town, we spotted two young bears playing. First they circled each other as if to say, "Hello." They nuzzled each other and one chewed a bit on the other's ear. Then they stood on their hind legs and moved about as if they were dancing. They started boxing, and then they fell down together and wrestled. After they finished playing, they stood up and shook off the snow like dogs. It looked like a small snowstorm! I was surprised that such powerful animals could be so gentle with each other.

At times like that, it's hard to remember that polar bears can be dangerous. Luckily, they don't hurt people very often. The people in town can feel safe if they follow the safety rules, such as staying off the streets when the bears are around.

I think when I grow up I would like to study polar bears. They are kind of scary. But they're also wonderful to watch. They are so huge, and they seem so smart. I'm really glad that I live in Churchill. How many kids can say that they have polar bears visiting their backyards?

# The Pudding like a Night on the Sea

ANN CAMERON

"I'm going to make something special for your mother," my father said.

My mother was out shopping. My father was in the kitchen, looking at the pots and the pans and the jars of this and that.

"What are you going to make?" I asked.

"A pudding," he said.

My father is a big man with wild, black hair. When he laughs, the sun laughs in the windowpanes. When he thinks, you can almost see his thoughts sitting on all of the tables and chairs. When he is angry, my little brother, Huey, and I shiver to the bottom of our shoes.

"What kind of pudding will you make?" Huey asked.

"A wonderful pudding," my father said. "It will taste

like a whole raft of lemons. It will taste like a night on
the sea."

Then he took out a knife and sliced five lemons in half.
He squeezed the first one. Juice squirted into my eye.

"Stand back!" he said, and he squeezed again. The
seeds flew out onto the floor. "Pick up those seeds, Huey!"
he said.

Huey took the broom and swept them up.

My father cracked some eggs and put the yolks into a
pan and the whites into a bowl. He rolled up his sleeves and
pushed back his hair and beat up the yolks. "Sugar, Julian!"
he said, and I poured in the sugar.

He went on beating. Then he put in lemon juice and
cream and set the pan on the stove. The pudding bubbled,
and he stirred it fast. Cream splashed on the stove. "Wipe
that up, Huey!" he said. Huey did.

It was hot by the stove. My father loosened his collar
and pushed at his sleeves. The stuff in the pan was getting
thicker and thicker. He held the beater up high in the
air. "Just right!" he said, as he sniffed in the smell of
the pudding.

He whipped the egg whites and mixed them into the
pudding. The pudding looked softer and lighter than air.

"Done!" he said. He washed all the pots, splashing
water on the floor, and wiped the counter so fast that his
hair made circles around his head.

"Perfect!" he said. "Now I'm going to take a nap. If something important happens, bother me. If nothing important happens, don't bother me. And—the pudding is for your mother. Leave the pudding alone!"

He went into the living room and was asleep in a minute, sitting straight up in his chair.

Huey and I guarded the pudding.

"Oh, it's a wonderful pudding," Huey said.

"With waves on the top like the ocean," I said.

"I wonder how it tastes," Huey said.

"Leave the pudding alone," I said.

"If I just put my finger in—there—I'll know how it tastes," Huey said.

And he did it.

"You did it!" I said. "How does it taste?"

"It tastes like a whole raft of lemons," he said. "It tastes like a night on the sea."

"You've made a hole in the pudding!" I said. "But since you did it, I'll have a taste." And it tasted like a whole night of lemons. It tasted like floating at sea.

"It's such a big pudding," Huey said. "It can't hurt to have a little more."

"Since you took more, I'll have more," I said.

"That was a bigger lick than I took!" Huey said. "I'm going to have more again."

"Whoops!" I said.

"You put in your whole hand!" Huey said. "Look at the pudding you spilled on the floor!"

"I am going to clean it up," I said. I took the rag from the sink.

"That's not really clean," Huey said.

"It's the best I can do," I said.

"Look at the pudding!" Huey said.

It looked like craters on the moon. "We have to smooth this over," I said. "So it looks the way it did before! Let's get spoons."

We evened the top of the pudding with spoons, and while we evened it, we ate some more.

"There isn't much left," I said.

"We were supposed to leave the pudding alone," Huey said.

"We'd better get away from here," I said. We ran into our bedroom and crawled under the bed. After a long time we heard my father's voice.

"Come into the kitchen, dear," he said. "I have something for you."

"Why, what is it?" my mother said, out in the kitchen.

Under the bed, Huey and I pressed ourselves to the wall.

"Look," said my father, "A wonderful pudding."

"Where is the pudding?" my mother said.

"WHERE ARE YOU BOYS?" my father said.

His voice went through every crack and corner of the house.

We felt like two leaves in a storm.

"'WHERE ARE YOU?' I SAID!" My father's voice was booming.

Huey whispered to me, "I'm scared."

We heard my father walking slowly through the rooms.

"Huey!" he called. "Julian!"

We could see his feet. He was coming into our room. He lifted the bedspread. There was his face—and his eyes like black lightning. He grabbed us by the legs and pulled. "STAND UP!" he said.

We stood.

"What do you have to tell me?" he said.

188

"We went outside," Huey said, "and when we came back, the pudding was gone!"

"Then why were you hiding under the bed?" my father said.

We didn't say anything. We looked at the floor.

"I can tell you one thing," he said. "There is going to be some beating here now! There is going to be some whipping!"

The curtains at the window were shaking. Huey was holding my hand.

"Go into the kitchen!" my father said. "Right now!"

We went into the kitchen.

"Come here, Huey!" my father said.

Huey walked toward him, his hands behind his back.

"See these eggs?" my father said. He cracked them and put the yolks in a pan and set the pan on the counter. He stood a chair by the counter. "Stand up here," he said to Huey.

Huey stood on the chair by the counter.

"Now it's time for your beating!" my father said.

Huey started to cry. His tears fell in with the egg yolks.

"Take this!" my father said. My father handed him the egg beater. "Now beat those eggs!" he said.

"Oh!" Huey said. He stopped crying and began beating the egg yolks.

"Now you, Julian, stand here!" my father said.

I stood on a chair by the table.

"Here!" he said, and he set the egg whites in front of me. "I want these whipped and whipped well!"

"Yes, sir!" I said and started whipping.

My father watched us. My mother came into the kitchen and watched us.

After a while Huey said, "This is hard work."

"That's too bad," my father said. "Your beating's not

done!" He added sugar and cream and lemon juice to Huey's pan and put the pan on the stove. Huey went on beating.

"My arm hurts from whipping," I said.

"That's too bad," my father said. "Your whipping's not done."

So I whipped and whipped, and Huey beat and beat.

"Hold that beater in the air, Huey!" my father said.

Huey held it in the air.

"See!" my father said. "A good pudding stays on the beater. It's thick enough now. Your beating's done." Then he turned to me. "Let's see those egg whites, Julian!" he said. They were puffed up and fluffy. "Congratulations, Julian!" he said. "Your whipping's done."

He mixed the egg whites into the pudding himself. Then he passed the pudding to my mother.

"This is wonderful pudding," she said. "Would you like some, boys?"

"No thank you," we said.

She picked up a spoon. "Why, this tastes like a whole raft of lemons," she said. "This tastes like a night on the sea."

# The Noblest Deed

GRANT LYONS

Once there was a very old man in Guadalajara who was about to die. He wanted to leave a diamond, the only wealth he had, to one of his three sons. But he could not decide which one. He called the three sons into his room, and this is what he told them.

"My sons, I am not a rich man. The only thing I have that is worth much is this diamond. It has been in our family for generations, and I would not want it sold. Because it cannot be sold or divided, I can give it to only one of you. The diamond will go to the one who accomplishes the noblest deed in a week's time. Go now. Return in a week to tell me what you have done."

A week passed, and the sons returned. They found their father even weaker than before and unable to leave his bed. He asked each in turn to tell his story.

"My father," said the first son, "I thought and thought of a deed that would be worthy. Finally, this is what I did. I gathered all my property, divided it in half, and gave one half to the poor people of the city."

The old man shook his head. "Ah, that is a good deed," he said, "but not truly noble. After all, it is every man's duty to be as generous as he can to the poor."

"*Padrecito*," said the second son, "when I was returning home from work one day, I saw a little girl caught

193

in the swift current of the Río Grande de Santiago. Though I can hardly swim myself, I jumped into the river and pulled her out. The current was so swift that I almost drowned."

"That, too, is a good deed, and yet not noble," said the father. "Every man should be willing to risk his life for the sake of a child."

Then the third son told his story. "Father, a wonderful thing happened to me. I was walking high up in the mountains very early one morning. There I saw a man, wrapped tight in a blanket, sleeping at the very edge of a cliff! I could hardly believe my eyes. If he turned this way or that, or if he moved at all in his sleep, the man would be certain to fall over the cliff, thousands of feet to the valley below! I crept closer, as quietly as I could, for I didn't want to startle him. And who do you think the man was? Sancho, my bitterest enemy! Many times he had threatened to kill me if he got the chance.

"I moved as close to him as I could. Gently I put my

arms around him. Suddenly his eyes opened and looked into mine. I saw he was afraid. 'Do not fear,' I said. With that I pulled him toward me and rolled with him, away from the cliff.

"We both stood up, and he said, '*Ay!* I came this way last night. It was so dark that I could not see my own feet! I was too tired to go on, so I stepped off the path to sleep. I had no idea where I was! I see now that if I had walked a little farther, or turned in my sleep, I would have become food for the vultures in the valley. You have saved my life, *amigo*—I, who had threatened to kill you!'

"We threw ourselves into each other's arms and swore to be friends forever. We wept for joy. Each of us found a friend, where before there had been an enemy!"

"Ah, my son!" exclaimed the old man. "That is a beautiful story and a truly noble deed. It is a rare man who will risk his life for the sake of an enemy. You are a noble man. The diamond is yours!"

# Beauty

E-YEH-SHURE'

Beauty is seen
In the sunlight,
The trees, the birds,
Corn growing and people working
Or dancing for their harvest.

Beauty is heard
In the night,
Wind sighing, rain falling,
Or a singer chanting
Anything in earnest.

Beauty is in yourself.
Good deeds, happy thoughts
That repeat themselves
In your dreams,
In your work,
And even in your rest.

196

# The Musical Palm Tree

ROBERT BARRY

Pablito and Alicia stretched high on tiptoe and looked out over the wall of the roof terrace of their house.

"See! There she comes," Alicia cried, pointing to a puff of smoke on the horizon. "The cruise ship *is* going to stop at San Juan today."

"This is my last chance," said Pablito. "Tomorrow is the Fiesta Patronal. I must earn two dollars more to buy the beautiful Spanish *mantilla* for Mamá to wear to the Fiesta."

"I saw it this morning in the shop window," said Alicia. "*Ay, qué linda!* How beautiful! Mamá must have it."

Pablito popped a big straw *pava* on his head. "I have to be at the dock when the ship arrives," he called over his shoulder as he dashed down the old stone stairway.

He ran through the narrow street. At the corner he stopped and pressed his nose against the window of La Casa de Oro. It was the finest shop in all of San Juan. Pablito had never been inside, but he had heard his mother admire the *mantilla* in the window. Only two dollars more, Pablito thought. I must hurry.

The big, white cruise ship was docking when he reached the pier. There was great excitement everywhere. Horns were tooting. Lines from the ship were being thrown ashore. A noisy crowd was gathering to meet the visitors. Pablito fought for a place in line as the gangplank was lowered and the visitors started to come ashore.

One of the guides shouted, "Let me take you to the beautiful beach at Luquillo."

Another called, "A trip to the mountains is better."

Pablito didn't say anything. Instead, he hoisted a little sign on a bamboo pole. The sign said: Let Pablito show you Puerto Rico. Only 25¢

A big man with broad shoulders laughed and asked, "What can you show an architect for twenty-five cents?"

Pablito lifted his *pava* and said, "*Bienvenido,* Señor.

Welcome to Puerto Rico. An architect makes grand houses, does he not?"

Pablito showed the architect some of the oldest buildings in San Juan. Then they went to see an ancient Spanish house that was being restored. Pablito ran up a winding stairway. "Look, Señor," he called, and he nodded toward a tree that grew inside the patio. "You could pick fruit for your breakfast each morning, right from this tree."

Reaching out, Pablito picked a guava from the tree and tossed it down. "Wouldn't you like to live here?" he asked.

"Magnificent!" the architect exclaimed. He was so delighted with the old Spanish house that he gave Pablito twenty-five cents, but he said that he wanted to stay and take some pictures.

Three sailors from the crew of the big ship were arguing on the dock when Pablito got back. They could not decide what they should see. The first sailor was pointing east. The second was pointing west. The third sailor was standing between the other two, shrugging his shoulders.

"Ahoy, mates," Pablito cried. "Follow me and I'll show you just what a sailor should see in San Juan."

The three sailors quickly fell in line behind Pablito. One after the other, they marched to the little plaza at the entrance to the city.

"This is Plaza de Colón," said Pablito. "It is named after the greatest sailor of all, Christopher Columbus." The sailors took a closer look at the statue in the center of the plaza. "He discovered Puerto Rico too," Pablito said proudly.

Pablito took the sailors to El Morro, the great Spanish fortress. He climbed on top of one of the big, black cannons while the sailors gathered around him. "This fort was built to keep enemy ships out of the harbor," Pablito explained. "If a pirate ship tried to sail past here, the Spanish soldiers would fire this cannon—*boom*—and sink the ship with a good shot."

Then Pablito told the sailors about Cofresí, the terrible pirate. "His treasure is still buried here," said Pablito, "in a cave on the south coast. But which cave, mates?—that's the question."

The three sailors were very excited about the pirate treasure. Each one gave Pablito a quarter before they marched off, one after the other, in a line—heading south.

Pablito was very hungry after his busy morning. He called up to Alicia from the narrow cobblestone street, and she lowered his lunch to him in a basket. "I must hurry," he called. "The ship will be leaving in a few hours."

Pablito found a cool place in the shade of the old sea wall before he looked inside his lunch bag. There were three little pies, still warm from the oven. "Just the thing for a working man," he said to himself.

After lunch there was no time to rest. Pablito took a tall lady visitor and her tiny white dog to see the huge stone "dog of the old fisherman."

"Many years ago, there was a dog who always went fishing with his master," Pablito told them. "One afternoon, the sea was very rough. The old fisherman decided to leave his dog behind. He told him to wait on the rock until he returned, but in the stormy sea, the old fisherman disappeared. The faithful dog, however, waited on the rock patiently. The dog was so still, and he waited so long, that finally he turned to stone himself."

Later in the afternoon, Pablito took a schoolteacher on a bus to Río Piedras for a tour of the university. When he got back to the city, however, it was late, and he still needed fifty cents for the beautiful Spanish *mantilla*.

Pablito saw a crowd near the entrance to the big El

201

Convento Hotel. In the center stood a small, dark-haired man with a cello.

"My name is Sternstein," Pablito heard him say to some of the guides in the crowd. "I play the cello in a symphony orchestra. Eight hours' practice—every day— even on the cruise ship! Is there something for me to see in Puerto Rico? Something to hear? Something soothing, musical . . . special?"

"I know a guitar player," one of the guides said. "He will play the most beautiful songs of the island for you."

"Oh no," Mr. Sternstein answered. "I have heard gypsy guitars played in Spanish caves. Surely his music cannot be better than that."

Another guide said, "I can take you to the beach at Boca de Cangrejos where the roar of the sea is like thunder."

"No, no," Mr. Sternstein answered impatiently. "I have heard the roar of the ocean on the rocks of Gay Head Light. Surely there is nothing to surpass that."

"Come with me to the rain forest," a third guide said. "There we can hear the song of the Puerto Rican wood warbler."

"I have heard the call of the ruddy red quail dove," said Mr. Sternstein. "What can be more beautiful than that?"

"I can show you a musical palm tree!" said Pablito.

"A palm tree . . . a musical palm tree!" Mr. Sternstein exclaimed. "That is something I have never seen—or heard."

"Come with me," said Pablito, and he took Mr. Sternstein by the hand. They hurried through the streets and along a narrow path that led out to the edge of the city. They puffed up to the top of a steep hill.

"This is the musical palm tree," said Pablito, and he stopped before an enormous, fan-shaped palm tree. "We must wait just a minute more. Let's rest, here under the tree."

They slumped down and leaned against the tree. The sun dropped slowly behind a range of misty mountaintops. The last glow of twilight lingered, and then a soft, sweet sound drifted down to them from the tree. *Co-quí. Co-quí. Co-quí-quí-quí.*

"What is it?" Mr. Sternstein whispered.

"It is the song of the tiny Puerto Rican tree frog, the *coquí*," said Pablito. "It is hidden in a leaf of this palm tree."

*Co-quí. Co-quí. Co-quí-quí-quí.*

Mr. Sternstein was delighted. "A heavenly note! I would like to play it on my cello," he said, taking his instrument out of its case. He was so happy that he gave Pablito *two* shiny quarters.

Pablito raced back to La Casa de Oro. Proudly he counted out eight shiny quarters. With the money he had already saved, this was just enough to buy the beautiful Spanish *mantilla*.

When Pablito gave the *mantilla* to his mother the next morning, he said, "See, Mamá, see what I found under a palm tree."

Pablito's mother smiled and shook her head gently. "Such a beautiful *mantilla*," she said, "you would never find under a palm tree."

"But Mamá, it was a musical palm tree," Pablito explained. "And under a musical palm tree, you can find the most wonderful things."

# Ramona's Book Report

### BEVERLY CLEARY

Ramona Quimby, eight years old and in the third grade, worried that her teacher thought she was a show-off and a nuisance. Now she had a new worry. Mrs. Whaley wanted the class to give book reports as though they were selling the books they had read. Ramona was not sure how to go about doing this.

The book, *The Left-Behind Cat,* which Mrs. Whaley had sent home for Ramona to read when she was sick, was divided into chapters but used babyish words. The story was about a cat left behind when a family moved away and about its adventures with a dog, another cat, and some children before it finally found a home with a nice, old couple who gave it a saucer of cream and named it Lefty because its left paw was white and because it had been left behind. Medium-boring, thought Ramona, good enough to pass the time on the bus, but not good enough to read during Sustained Silent Reading.

"Daddy, how do you sell something?" Ramona interrupted her father, who was studying, even though she knew she should not. However, her need for an answer was urgent.

Mr. Quimby did not look up from his book. "You ought to know. You see enough commercials on television."

Ramona considered his answer. She had always looked upon commercials as entertainment, but now she thought about some of her favorites—the cats that danced back and forth, the dog that pushed away 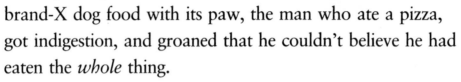 brand-X dog food with its paw, the man who ate a pizza, got indigestion, and groaned that he couldn't believe he had eaten the *whole* thing.

"Do you mean I should do a book report like a TV commercial?" Ramona asked.

"Why not?" Mr. Quimby answered in an absent-minded way.

"I don't want my teacher to say I'm a nuisance," said Ramona, needing assurance from a grownup.

This time Mr. Quimby lifted his eyes from his book. "Look," he said, "she told you to pretend you're selling the book, so sell it. What better way than through a TV commercial? You aren't being a nuisance if you do what your teacher asks."

Ramona went to her room and looked at her table, which the family called "Ramona's studio." It was a clutter of crayons, different kinds of paper, tape, bits of yarn, and odds and ends that Ramona used for amusing herself. Then Ramona thought a moment, and suddenly, filled with inspiration, she went to work. She knew exactly what she wanted to do and set about doing it. She worked with paper, crayons, tape, and rubber bands. She worked so hard and with such pleasure that her cheeks grew pink. Nothing in the whole world felt as good as being able to make something from a sudden idea.

Finally, with a big sigh of relief, Ramona leaned back in her chair to admire her work. She had made three cat masks with holes for eyes and mouths, masks that could be worn by hooking rubber bands over ears. But Ramona did not stop there. With pencil and paper, she began to write out what she would say. Next she phoned Sara and Janet and explained her plan to them. Both friends giggled and agreed to take part in the book report. Ramona spent the rest of the evening memorizing what she was going to say.

At school the next morning Ramona slipped cat masks to Sara and Janet and waited for book reports to begin.

After arithmetic, Mrs. Whaley called on several people

to come to the front of the room to pretend they were selling books to the class. Most of the reports began, "This is a book about . . ." and many ended with ". . . if you want to find out what happens next, read the book."

Then Mrs. Whaley said, "We have time for one more report before lunch. Who wants to be next?"

Ramona waved her hand, and Mrs. Whaley nodded.

Ramona beckoned to Sara and Janet, who giggled in an embarrassed way but joined Ramona, standing behind her and off to one side. All three girls slipped on their cat masks and giggled again. Ramona took a deep breath as Sara and Janet began to chant, "*Meow,* meow, meow, meow. *Meow,* meow, meow, meow," and danced back and forth like the cats they had seen in the cat-food commercial on television.

"*Left-Behind Cat* gives kids something to smile about," said Ramona in a loud, clear voice, while her chorus meowed softly behind her. She wasn't sure that what she said was exactly true, but neither were the commercials that showed cats eating dry cat food without making any noise. "Kids who have tried *Left-Behind Cat* are all smiles, smiles, smiles. *Left-Behind Cat* is the book kids ask for by name. Kids can read it every day and thrive on it. The happiest kids read *Left-Behind Cat. Left-Behind Cat* contains cats, dogs, people—" Here Ramona caught sight of Danny leaning back in his seat, grinning in the way that always flustered her. She could not help interrupting herself with a giggle, and after suppressing it she tried not to look at Danny and to take up where she had left off: ". . . cats, dogs, people—" The giggle came back, and Ramona was lost. She could not remember what came next. ". . . cats, dogs, people," she repeated, trying to start and failing.

Mrs. Whaley and the class waited. Danny grinned. Ramona's loyal chorus meowed and danced. This performance could not go on all morning. Ramona had to say something, anything, to end the waiting, the meowing, her book report. She tried desperately to recall a cat-food

commercial, any cat-food commercial, and could not. All she could remember was the man on television who ate the pizza, and so she blurted out the only sentence she could think of: "I can't believe I read the *whole* thing!"

Mrs. Whaley's laugh rang out above the laughter of the class. Ramona felt her face turn red behind her mask, and her ears, visible to the class, turned red as well.

"Thank you, Ramona," said Mrs. Whaley. "That was most entertaining. Class, you are excused for lunch."

Ramona felt brave behind her cat mask. "Mrs. Whaley," she said, as the class pushed back chairs and gathered up lunch boxes, "that wasn't the way my report was supposed to end."

"Did you like the book?" asked Mrs. Whaley.

"Not really," confessed Ramona.

"Then I think it was a good way to end your report," said the teacher. "Asking the class to sell books they really don't like isn't fair, now that I stop to think about it. I was only trying to make book reports a little livelier." She smiled at Ramona. "Now run along and eat your lunch."

Ramona snatched up her lunch box and went jumping down the stairs to the cafeteria. She laughed to herself because she knew exactly what all the boys and girls from her class would say when they finished their lunches. She knew because she planned to say it herself: "I can't believe I ate the *whole* thing!"

# Glossary

# Pronunciation Key

| | | | | |
|---|---|---|---|---|
| a_, ă_ | apple, tan | g | gas, wiggle, sag |
| ā | acorn, table | ġ | gem, giant, gym |
| ȧ | alone, Donna | gh_ | ghost |
| â | air, care | _gh | though, thought (silent) |
| ä | father, wand | h_ | hat |
| a̱ | all, ball | i_, ĭ_ | it, sit |
| a_e | ape, bake | ī | pilot, pie |
| ai_ | aim, sail | _ï_ | babies, machine, *also* |
| ȧr | calendar | | onion, savior, familiar |
| är | art, park, car | i_e | ice, bite |
| au_ | author, Paul | _igh | high, bright |
| aw | awful, lawn, saw | ir | irk, bird, fir |
| _ay | say, day | j_ | jam |
| b | bat, able, tub | k | kite, ankle, ink |
| c | cat, cot, cut | kn_ | knife |
| ce | cent, ace | l | lamp, wallet, tail |
| ch | chest, church | _le | table, ample |
| c̄h | chorus, ache | m | man, bump, ham |
| ch̆ | chute | _mb | lamb, comb |
| c̆i | cider, decide | n | no, tent, sun |
| _c̱i_ | special | _n̄_ | uncle, anger |
| _ck | tack, sick | _ng | sing, ring |
| cy | bicycle | o_, ŏ_ | odd, pot |
| d | dad | ō | go, no, toe |
| _dge | edge, judge | ȯ | come, wagon |
| e_, ĕ_ | elf, hen | ô | off, song |
| ē | equal, me | oa_ | oat, soap |
| ė | moment, loaded | o_e | ode, bone |
| ea | eat, leap, tea | oi_ | oil, boil |
| _ĕa_ | head, bread | o̽o̽ | book, nook |
| ee | eel, feet, see | o̅o̅ | boot, zoo |
| er | herd, her | or | order, normal |
| _ew | few, blew | ȯr | motor, doctor |
| f | far, taffy, off | ou_ | out, hound |

| | | | |
|---|---|---|---|
| ow | owl, town, cow | ū̇ | truth, true |
| _ōw | low, throw | u̇ | nature |
| _oy | boy, toy | u̲ | pull, full |
| p | paper, tap | ur | urge, turn, fur |
| ph | phone, elephant, graph | ūr | cure, pure |
| qu_ | quick, queen | v | voice, save |
| r | ram, born, ear | w_ | will, wash |
| s | sun, ask, yes | wh_ | white, what |
| _s̲ | toes, hose | wr_ | write |
| _s̲_ | vision, confusion | _x | extra, ax |
| ss̲ | fission | _x̲_ | exist, example |
| sh | show, bishop, fish | y_ | yes, yet |
| t | tall, sets, bit | _y | baby, happy (when |
| th | thick, three | | it is the only |
| th̲ | this, feather, bathe | | vowel in a final |
| _tch | itch, patch | | unstressed |
| _ti̲_ | nation, station, | | syllable) |
| | *also* question | _y̆_ | cymbal |
| t̲u | congratulate | _ȳ | cry, sky |
| u_, ŭ_ | up, bus | ẏ | zephyr, martyr |
| ū | use, cute, *also* granulate | z | zoo, nozzle, buzz |

1. If a word ends in a silent *e*, as in **face**, the silent *e* is not marked. If a word ends in -*ed* pronounced **t**, as in **baked**, or **d**, as in **stayed**, no mark is needed. If the ending -*ed* forms a separate syllable pronounced ėd, as in **load′ėd**, the *e* has a dot.

2. If there are two or three vowels in the same syllable and only one is marked, as in **beaū′ty, friĕnd, rōgue**, or **breāk**, all the other vowels in the syllable are silent.

3. The Open Court diacritical marks in the Pronunciation Key make it possible to indicate the pronunciation of most unfamiliar words without respelling.

**Ab·o·riġ'i·nē** *n.* a member of an Australian tribe

**ab'sėnt-mīnd'ėd** *adj.* not paying attention; forgetful

**ac·cȯm'pȧ·ny** *v.* to go along with

**ac·com'plish** *v.* to achieve; to get something done

**ac'cū·rȧte** *adj.* correct

**A.D.** an abbreviation for the Latin words for "in the year of our Lord" or since the birth of Jesus (*See also* **B.C.**)

**ad·vance'** *v.* to move forward

**ad·vīs'ȯr** *n.* a person who makes useful suggestions (*Also spelled* **adviser.**)

**Af·ghan'i·stan'** *n.* a country in Asia between India and the Soviet Union

**Af'ri·cȧ** *n.* one of the seven main bodies of land in the world

**aġe** *n.* a long amount of time

**A·hoy', mates.** a way that sailors say "Hello there, friends."

**Ä·ï'kō**

**âir'strip** *n.* a smooth, straight strip of land that airplanes take off and land on

**A·las'kȧ** *n.* the most northern state in the United States

**Ä·lï'cï·ä**

**Äl'lȧh** *n.* the Islamic name for "God"

**ȧ·mï'gō** *n.* a Spanish word for "friend"

**an·noyed** (ȧ·noid') *adj.* bothered; a bit angry

**Ant·ärc'ti·cȧ** (*or* ant·är'ti·cȧ) *n.* the large body of land around the South Pole

**ȧp·par'ėnt·ly** *adv.* clearly; seemingly

**Ar'ȧ·bic** *n.* a language spoken in northern Africa

**är'chē·ol'ȯ·ġist** *n.* a person who studies how people lived long ago (*Also spelled* **archaeologist.**)

**är'chi·tect** *n.* a person who designs buildings

**Ärc'tic** (*or* är'tic) **O·cean** (ō'shȧn) *n.* the large body of water around the North Pole

**Är'ġen·tï'nä** *n.* a large country in South America

**ȧ·ris̱e'** *v.* to get up

**ȧr·rī'vȧl** *n.* the act of coming to a place

**Ā'sïä** *n.* the largest of the seven main bodies of land in the world

**Ā'sïä Mï'nȯr** *n.* the area between the Mediterranean and Black seas

**as·sur·ance** (ȧ·shūr'ȧnce) *n.* a feeling of comfort or sureness

**Ȧt·lan'tic O·cean** (ō'shȧn) *n.* the huge body of water east of North and South America

**at′mŏs•phēre** *n.* the air

**åt•tend′ to** (tū) *v.* to take care of

**Aus•tral•ia** (aus•trāl′yà) *n.* a large island country between the Pacific and Indian oceans

**Aus′trĭ•å** *n.* a country near Germany

**å•void′** *v.* to keep away from

**Ay,** (ī) **qué** (ke) **lĭn′dä!** the Spanish words for "Oh, how lovely!"

**bä′bä** n. a Swahili (African) word for "father"

**Bac′chus** *n.* the god of wine in ancient Roman stories

**back′ground** *n.* a person's past

**Bäl′bus**

**bal′cò•ny** *n.* a porch off an upper side of a building

**bal•let** (ba•lā′) *n.* a kind of dancing often done for an audience

**bam•boo′** *n.* a tall plant that has hard, hollow stems

**ban•dan′nà** *n.* a large, brightly colored scarf

**ban′ish** *v.* to send away

**bär•bâr′ĭ•ån** *n.* a wild and cruel person

**Bas′tet** *n.* a goddess of the ancient Egyptians, often pictured as a cat

**Pronunciation Key**

VOWELS: sat, hăve, āble, fäther, all, câre, ålone; yet, brĕad, mē, loadèd; it, practĭce, pīlot, machīne; hot, nō, ôff, wagòn; fŏot, fōod; oil, toy; count, town; up, ūse, trŭth, pull; mўth, baby, crў, zephўr.

CONSONANTS: cent, cider, cycle; chorus, chute; ġem; light and though (silent), ghost; iňk; elephant; toes; them; special, measure, nation, nature.

**B.C.** an abbreviation for the Latin words for "before Christ" or before the birth of Jesus. (*See also* **A.D.**)

**bē′ing** *n.* a living thing

**bel′lōw** *v.* to roar or shout

**best-bė•lŏv′ed** (*or* bė•luvd′) *adj.* favorite

**bil•lion** (bil′yun) *n.* one thousand million or a very large number

**bite ôff mōre than one** (wun) **can chew** to try to do more than one can handle

**Black Dĕath** *n.* a disease that killed many during the Middle Ages (*See also* **bubonic plague.**)

**blaze** *n.* a sudden, bright glow

**blis′ter** *v.* to cause a bubble on the skin

**bliz′zård** *n.* a heavy snowstorm with strong winds and cold temperatures

**blot out** *v.* to darken or cover

**bluff** *n.* a show made to try to fool —*v.* to try to fool

**Bō′cä de Cangrejos** (cän•gre′hōs)

**boōm′er•ang** *n.* a curved stick that can be thrown so as to come back

**bor′der** *v.* to lie alongside

**brace** *v.* to steady or hold firm

**breed** *v.* to raise

**bril′li̇ant** *adj.* bright; glittering

**bring or′der** *v.* to arrange

**bū•bon′ic plague** (plāg) *n.* a disease spread by the fleas on rats

**bur′rō** *n.* a small donkey

**bush** *n.* the central desert of Australia

**bush′ hat** *n.* a brimmed hat often worn in the jungle

**busi•ness** (bis′ness) **is̱ mov•ing** (mū̱v′ing) things are being bought and sold

**Can′a̱•da̱** *n.* the large country north of the United States

**Ca̱•nā′di̱•a̱n** *n.* a citizen of Canada

**cär′gō** *n.* goods carried from place to place

**Câr•ib•bē′an** *or* **Ca̱•rib′bē•a̱n Is•lands** (ī′la̱nds̱) *n. pl.* a group of islands in the Caribbean Sea

**Cär•när′vȯn** *n.* Lord Carnarvon, a man whose money helped in the discovery of the tomb of Tutankhamen

**cast** *v.* to throw

**Ca•thay′** *n.* an old name for China

**cau′ti̇ȯus•ly** *adv.* carefully

**cen′ti•mē•ter** *n.* a length of about one-third of an inch

**cen′tū•ry** *n.* one hundred years

**cha̱n•de̱•li̇er′** *n.* a fancy hanging lamp

**Chao** (jow) *n.* one of the ancient kingdoms in what is now China

**Chao Kao** (jow gow)

**chäṙge** *v.* to rush forward or attack —*n.* an attack

**châr′i̇•ȯt** *n.* in ancient times, a two-wheeled vehicle pulled by horses

**Cheng** (jung) *n.* the king who united many kingdoms into the country of China

**Ch′ï** *n.* one of the ancient kingdoms in what is now China

**Ch′in** *n.* one of the ancient kingdoms in what is now China

**Chī′na̱** *n.* a very large country near India and Japan

**Ch′in Shïh** (sher) **Huang** (hwäng) **Ti** (di̇) *n.* the first emperor of China

**Cho•pin** (shō•pan′) *n.* Frederic Chopin, a Polish writer of music

**chop′sticks** *n. pl.* a pair of sticks held in one hand for eating with

**Chou** (jō) *n.* one of the ancient kingdoms in what is now China

**Chris′ti•an′i•ty** *n.* the religion taught by Christ and his followers

**Chris′to•pher Co•lum′bus** *n.* one of the first explorers of North America

**Ch′ụ** *n.* one of the ancient kingdoms in what is now China

**civ′i•li•zā′tion** *n.* the way a group of people using the same laws and language lives together

**clī′mate** *n.* the usual weather of an area

**coast′al** *adj.* in the area where land and sea meet

**côf′fee house′** *n.* a cafe where coffee and snacks are served

**Co•fre•sí** (cō•fre•sï′)

**col•lide′** *v.* to crash into each other

**col′or•ful** *adj.* interesting

**com•bine′** *v.* to bring or put together

**come to** (tụ̄) **pass′** to happen

**com•mer′cial** *n.* an advertisement

**com•plain′** *v.* to talk about what seems wrong

**con•ceal′** *v.* to hide

**con•fess′** *v.* to admit

**Coñ′gō** *n.* another spelling for **Kongo**, the name of an African language

**con•nect′** *v.* 1. to join the parts of 2. to think of one thing as the cause of another

**con•quer** (coñ′ker) *v.* to defeat in battle

**con•sent′** *n.* permission

**con•sid′er** *v.* to think about

**con′stant** *adj.* steady

**con′ti•nent** *n.* one of the seven large areas of land on the earth

**con•tin′ū•al•ly** *adv.* happening over and over

**cō•op′er•ā′tion** *n.* working together for the same purpose

**co•quí** (cō•kï′) *n.* 1. a tree frog of Puerto Rico 2. the sound the Puerto Rican tree frog makes

**co•rō′na** *n.* a ring of light around the moon during a total eclipse of the sun (*See also* **eclipse**.)

**coun′ter•pane** *n.* a quilt or a bedspread

**cran′ny** *n.* a small opening in a wall

**crop** *n.* a plant that is raised for use or sale

217

**crown** *n.* a head covering for a king or queen

**crўs′tȧl** *adj.* made of fine, clear glass

**cul′tὺre** *n.* the way a certain group of people lives

**cun′ning** *n.* cleverness

**cur′rėnt** *n.* the flow of a body of water

**curse** *v.* to speak in anger against —*n.* a wish for something bad to happen to someone

**czar•das** (chär′däsh) *n.* a Hungarian folk dance

**Czech•o•slo•va•ki•a** (chech′ȯ•slȯ•vä′kï•ȧ) *n.* a country near Poland

**dale** *n.* a valley

**dañ′gle** *v.* to hang loosely

**därk′est Pė•rӯ′** a part of the South American country of Peru that is far from any cities

**daz′zling** *adj.* shining

**dĕad′ly** *adj.* able to cause death

**debt** (det) *n.* an amount of money owed

**dė•cree′** *v.* to make a law —*n.* an order

**deed** *n.* an act

**dė•moc′rȧ•cy** *n.* a form of government in which the people vote

**dė•pend′** *v.* to count on for help

**dė•spair′** *n.* hopelessness

**dė•tail′** *or* dē′tail *n.* a small task in a large job

**dė•ter′mĭned** *adj.* having one's mind strongly made up

**dė•vel′ȯp** *v.* 1. to make something for the first time 2. to teach oneself how to do something a special way 3. to grow, change, or improve

**dė•vour′** *v.* to eat up

**dif′fi•cult to** (tӯ) **man′ȧ•ge** hard to govern

**di•ġest′** *v.* to use food for energy

**dig′ni•târ•y** *n.* an important person in government

**di•rect′ly** *adv.* in a straight line

**dis•ease′** *n.* an illness

**dis•lodge′** *v.* to force out of place

**dis′tȧnt** *adj.* far away

**dis•tiñct′ly** *adv.* clearly

**dis•tin•guished** (dis•tiñ′gwished) *adj.* special or well-known

**dome** *n.* a shape like an upside-down bowl

**dȯ•mes′tic** *adj.* tame; raised or kept by people

**drill** *n.* a way of learning through practice

**drove** *n.* a large, moving group

**ėar′ly** *adj.* far back in time

**earn one's** (wuns) **keep** to do something useful in exchange for food and shelter

**earth'en** *adj.* made of dirt

**e·clipse'** *n.* a darkening of the sun or moon for a short time

**ee'rie** *adj.* strange or unnatural

**E'gypt** *n.* a country in northern Africa

**E·gyp'tian** *n.* a person from Egypt —*adj.* from or having to do with Egypt

**e·lec·tron'ic beep'er** *n.* a small machine that sends sound signals

**El Mor'rō** *n.* a famous, old fort in Puerto Rico

**em'i·grate** *v.* to leave one's own country to live in another

**em'pire** *n.* a large area ruled by one person

**en·chant'ed** *adj.* under a magical spell

**Eng'land** *n.* a country in Britain, in northern Europe

**Eng'lish** *n.* the language of England and many other countries

**en·ter·tain'** *v.* to treat as a guest

**e·rupt'** *v.* to explode

**E·thi·ō'pi·a** *n.* a country in northeastern Africa next to Egypt

**Eur'ope** *n.* one of the seven main bodies of land in the world

**Pronunciation Key**

VOWELS: sat, hăve, āble, fäther, all, câre, alone; yet, brĕad, mē, loadèd; it, practĭce, pīlot, machĭne; hot, nō, ôff, wagòn; foŏt, fōōd; oil, toy; count, town; up, ūse, trŭth, pull; mўth, baby, crў, zephýr.

CONSONANTS: cent, cider, cycle; chorus, chute; gem; light and though (silent), ghost; iňk; elephant; toes; them; special, measure, nation, nature.

**Eur'o·pē'an** *adj.* belonging to the group of countries that make up Europe —*n.* a person from Europe

**ex·ist'** *v.* to continue to be

**ex·ŏ'tic** *adj.* foreign or unusual

**ex'pla·nā'tion** *n* the reasons for something

**ex·traôr'di·nâr·y** *adj.* very unusual

**fab'ū·lous** *adj.* amazing or wonderful

**face** *v.* to cover the front of something

**faint'ly** *adv.* softly

**fer'tĭle** *adj.* rich; able to grow healthy plants

**fes·tiv'i·ty** *n.* a celebration

**Fï·es'tä Pä·trō·näl'** *n.* a festival to honor the person for whom a town has been named

**fil'ter** *n.* something that blocks harmful light rays —*v.* to block out

**flee** *v.* to run away

**fleet** *n.* a group of ships

**flus′ter** *v.* to make nervous or confused

**fol′ly** *n.* foolishness

**for·bid′** *v.* to order against

**force** *n.* strength or power

**fore′ground** *n.* what can be seen in the front of a picture

**for·eign** (fōr′in) *adj.* having to do with another country

**France** *n.* a country in western Europe

**frank′furt·er** *n.* a long, thin sausage often eaten on a roll

**French** *n.* the language of France and many other countries

**frock** *n.* a dress

**Fū Sū** *n.* the oldest son of the first emperor of China

**Gä** *n.* an African language

**game′ war′den** *n.* a person whose job includes protecting wild animals

**gāp′ing** *adj.* open wide

**gär′land** *n.* a circle of flowers or leaves used as decoration

**gär′ment** *n.* a piece of clothing

**gath′er one's** (wuns) **cour′age** to convince oneself to be brave

**gen·er·ā′tion** *n.* 1. a group of persons or animals born at about the same time 2. the time between the birth of parents and that of their children

**gifts of** (ov) **thē earth and plĕa′sure of** (ov) **hū′man com′pa·ny** nature and friendship

**glee′ful·ly** *adv.* joyfully

**glim′mer** *n.* a flash

**glis·ten** (glis′en) *v.* to shine

**gloom′y** *adj.* dark; sad

**goods** *n. pl.* things bought and sold

**gov′ern·ment** *n.* the ruling of a country

**grad·u·al·ly** (graj′ū·al·ly) *av.* little by little

**gran′ny** *n.* a grandmother

**Greece** *n.* a country in southern Europe

**green** *adj.* growing; not dead and dry

**grief** *n.* great sadness

**grove** *n.* a small group of trees

**growth** *n.* a group of growing plants

**hai·ku** (hī′kū) *n.* a kind of Japanese poem that has three lines and seventeen syllables

**Hāi′ti** *n.* a country on an island in the Atlantic Ocean, south of the United States

220

**Ham′e·lin** *n.* a town in Germany

**Hän** *n.* one of the ancient kingdoms in what is now China

**Hän′sï**

**här′bòr** *n.* a safe place for tying up ships

**här′mò·ny** *n.* a pleasing arrangement

**haugh′ty** *adj.* acting as though one is better than others

**Hau·sa** (how′sä) *n.* an African language

**Her′cū·lā′nē·um** *n.* a town in Italy destroyed by the eruption of Vesuvius in the year A.D. 79

**Her′cū·lēs′** *n.* a very strong hero in old stories

**hes′i·tate** *v.* to wait a moment

**hide** *n.* the skin of a large animal such as a cow

**hī·er·ò·glÿph′ics** *n. pl.* a kind of writing that uses pictures instead of letters

**Hi·pol·y·te** (hi·pol′i·te′)

**his·tōr′ic** *adj.* well-known or interesting because of things that happened in the past

**his′tò·ry** *n.* all that has happened in the past

**Hod′jä** *n.* 1. a Middle Eastern title for a wise man 2. a Middle Eastern character who sometimes acts smart and sometimes foolish

**hoist** *v.* to raise or lift

**hōrde** *n.* a large group

**hò·rī′zòn** *n.* a faraway line where the earth or sea seems to meet the sky

**horse′rad·ish** *n.* a sauce made from the strong-tasting root of a plant

**hōst** *n.* one who offers guests food or a place to stay

**hu′mòr** *v.* to go along with what someone wants or believes —*n.* the ability to see or enjoy what is funny

**hurl** *v.* to throw with great strength

**ice′flōe′** *n.* a large piece of floating ice

**il·lē′gàl·ly** *adv.* in a way that breaks a law

**im′aġe** *n.* a picture or copy of a real thing

**im·aġ′i·nâr′y** *adj.* present only in the mind

**im·aġ′ïne** *v.* to guess

221

Ĭ'mō *n.* the name of a monkey that was studied by certain scientists

im•pā'tient•ly *adv.* not willing to wait

im•prove (im•prūv') *v.* to make better

in•creas'ing•ly *adv.* more and more

In'dï•à *n.* a very large country near China and Japan

in'lànd *adj.* away from the ocean

in'ner *adj.* in the center

in•spi•rā'tiòn *n.* a sudden, good idea

in•vade' *v.* to enter by force

in vain' without success

ir•reg'ū•làr *adj.* unusual; not the way things are normally done

Is'làm *n.* the religion taught by Mohammed and his followers

Jà•pan' *n.* a country on a group of islands near China

jĕal'òus•y *n.* hatred caused by wanting what another has

Jō'nàh *n.* in a Bible story, the hero who was eaten by a huge fish

Jop'pà *n.* the old name of a port in Israel

Jo•se•fi•na (hō•se•fï'nä)

jòur'nàl•ist *n.* writer for newspapers or magazines

joy'òus *adj.* very happy

Jū'dà•iṣm *n.* the religion taught by Moses and the Hebrew people

kañ•gà•rōō' *n.* an Australian animal that has powerful back legs and can jump a long way

Kä•nu̱'rï *n.* an African language

keen *adj.* sharp; better than average

keep *n.* food and shelter, or the money needed for them

keep'er of (òv) thè seals̲ *n.* the person who guards the designs with which a ruler marks his property

Kēn'yà *n.* a country in eastern Africa

kil'ò•gram *n.* a weight of about two pounds

ki•mō'nō *n.* a kind of loose robe tied with a wide, cloth belt

kō•ä'là *n.* a small, furry, gray animal that lives in trees in Australia

Kō'shi•mä *n.* a Japanese island

ku̱'ku̱s *n. pl.* the Swahili (African) word for "chickens"

Lä Cä'sä de Ō'rō *n.* Spanish words for "The House of Gold"

lā'dèn *adj.* loaded

land'scape *n.* a view of the land

lan•guage (lañ'gwàġe) *n.* the speech of people in a certain country or place

law'māk'er *n.* a person who makes the rules of a country

lay'èred *adj.* one above the other

**lĕad′ėn** *adj.* made of the metal lead

**lens** *n.* a clear part behind the dark center of the eye

**Liao•dong** (lĭ•ow•dōong′) *n.* a town in China

**life′boat′** *n.* a boat carried on a large ship, to be used for rescuing

**Lĭ′mä** *n.* the capital city of Peru

**line** *n.* a rope having one end tied to a ship

**lin•tao** (lin•dou′) *n.* a town in China

**Lĭ Ssŭ**

**Lȯn′dȯn** *n.* the capital city of England

**lop′sĭd•ėd** *adj.* uneven; out of balance

**lot** *n.* an object used to decide something by luck

**Lū** *n.* one of the ancient kingdoms in what is now China

**Lū′cius**

**lū′nȧr val′lēy** *n.* one of the valleys on the moon

**Lux′ėm•bȯurg** *n.* a tiny country near France and Germany

**ma•caque** (mȧ•cak′) *n.* a kind of monkey

**mag•nif′i•cėnt** *adj.* very beautiful or fancy

**Ma•jor•ca** (mȧ•yor′cȧ) *n.* an island near Spain

**mañ′gō** *n.* a tropical fruit tree

**Man′i•tō′bȧ** *n.* an area in the middle of Canada

**man•til•la** (man•tĭ′yä) *n.* a kind of lace head scarf

**mär′mȧ•lade** *n.* a kind of jam made of fruit such as oranges

**Ma•sai** (mȧ•sī′) *n.* an African language spoken in Kenya and Tanzania

**mĕas′ure** *n.* the size of something

**Med′i•ter•rā′nē•ȧn** *n.* the area around the Mediterranean Sea— *adj.* from the area around the Mediterranean Sea

**mem′ȯ•rȧ•ble** *adj.* not easily forgotten

**Meng Tïän** (mung dĭ′en) *n.* the grand general under the emperor who built the Great Wall of China

**mer′chȧn•dise** *or* **mer′chȧn•dise** *n.* things that are for sale

**mer′chȧnt** *n.* a person who buys and sells for a living

**mer′ci•ful** *adj.* showing kindness

**mē′ter** *n.* a length of about three feet

**Met′tė Gäd** *n.* the wife of the artist Paul Gauguin

**Mex′i•cō′** *n.* the large country south of the United States

**Mī′dàs** *n.* a king in an ancient Greek story

**might′y** *adj.* strong

**mīld** *adj.* not too hot and not too cold

**Milk′y Way′** *n.* a group of stars that looks like milk spilled across the night sky

**mill′ wheels′** *n. pl.* a pair of large, stone wheels that, when turned, grind grain between them

**min′is•ter** *n.* an important person who helps in government

**Mi•se′num** *n.* an ancient port in Italy

**mis̲′er•y** *n.* great unhappiness

**mis•for′tùne** *n.* bad luck

**mist** *n.* a thin fog

**mod′ėrn** *adj.* not old-fashioned

**Moñ′gòl** *n.* a member of the tribes that once roamed Russia, Persia, and China

**mos•qui•to** (mòs•kï′tō) **net′** *n.* a fine net often draped around a bed in tropical areas to keep mosquitos away while one is sleeping

**mound** *n.* a pile of dirt or stones

**moun′tàin rānġe′** *n.* a line of mountains

**mum′my** *n.* a dead body wrapped and dried in a special way

**mur′mur** *v.* to make a low, soft sound

**nâr′rōw** *v.* to become thinner

**nat′ū•ràl** *adj.* made up of something in nature

**Nē•a′pō•lis** *n.* an ancient name for the Italian city of Naples

**near′-sight′ėd** *adj.* unable to see things that are far away

**nee′dle•wòrk′** *n.* sewing that is done by hand

**nev′er•the̲•less′** *adv.* but; in spite of that

**Nin′ė•vėh** *n.* an ancient city in the country that is now called Iraq

**nō′ble** *adj.* showing greatness

**nō′mad** *n.* a person who lives by wandering from place to place

**Nō′nï•à**

**nook** *n.* a corner

**North′ Pole′** *n.* the most northern point of the world

**nu̲′mer•òus** *adj.* many in number

**òf•fend′** *v.* to insult

**or′bit** *n.* the steady path that a planet, moon, or satellite follows around another object in space

**os′trich** *n.* a large, fast-running African bird having a long neck and legs

**out′back′** *n.* the central desert of Australia

**ō′ver•cȯme′** *adj.* won over: worn out

**ō•ver•flōw′** *v.* to run over

**Pä•blı̆′tō**

**Pȧ•cif′ic** *n.* the countries and islands in the Pacific Ocean

**Pac•tō′lus** *n.* a small river in Asia Minor

**Pä•dre•cı̆′tō** *n.* a Spanish word for "Daddy"

**pȧ•les′trȧ** *n.* a public place for watching sports in ancient times

**Päl′mä** *n.* a town on the island of Majorca near Spain

**pan′ic** *v.* to become so frightened that one behaves without thinking clearly

**pär′cel** *n.* a package

**Paul Gau•guin** (gō•gan′) *n.* a painter famous for his tropical scenes in bright colors

**pä′vä** *n.* a kind of hat worn in Puerto Rico

**peer** *v.* to look closely

**pen′ė•trate** *v.* to go into and through

**per•fūme′** *v.* to make to smell good

**per•suade** (per•swade′) *v.* to convince

**Pe•rū̱′** *n.* a country in western South America

**Pe•rū̱′vı̈•ȧn** *adj.* from the country of Peru

**Phil′ip•pı̄ne′ Is•lands** (ı̄′lands) *n. pl.* a group of islands in the Pacific Ocean southeast of China

**Phrў′g̣ı̈•ȧ** *n.* an ancient country in what is now Turkey

**pı̄ed** *adj.* dressed in clothes of many colors

**piēr** *n.* a landing place that ships or boats can be tied to

**pı̄p′er** *n.* a person who plays a kind of flute

**plain** *n.* an area of flat land

**plas′ter** *v.* to spread thickly

**pla•teau** (plă•tō′) *n.* a high plain

**plat′form** *n.* a raised area next to railroad tracks, from which passengers enter or leave train cars

**plat′y•pus** *n.* a furry, brown animal with webbed feet and a bill like a duck

**plä′zä** *or* **pla′zä** *n.* a town square; an open area in a town or city

**Pla′za** (plä′sä) **de Co•lón** (cô•lôn′) *n.* a town square in San Juan, Puerto Rico, named for Christopher Columbus

**plunġe** *v.* to dip or dive

**poach′er** *n.* a person who un-lawfully kills animals

**pol′ȯ•naise′** *n.* 1. a slow Polish dance 2. the music for such a dance

**pop•ū•lā′tiȯn** *n.* the number of people who live in an area

**pȯrt** *n.* a city where ships are loaded and unloaded

**Pȯr′tu̇•ġȧl**

**Por•tu•guese** (pȯr′tu̇•gēs′) *n.* the language of Portugal and Brazil

**prep•a•rā′tiȯn** *n.* n. something that must be done to get ready

**prė•pare′** *v.* to get [food] ready for eating

**prė•poc′er•ȯs** *adj.* a humorous spelling of "preposterous" to rhyme with "rhinoceros" (*See* **preposterous.**)

**prė•pos′ter•ȯus** *adj.* ridiculous

**prey** (prā) *n.* animals that are hunted and killed for food

**prime min′is•ter** *n.* the highest elected person in certain governments

**prō•con′sul** *n.* a governor of an area in ancient Roman times

**prȯ•fes′siȯn•ȧl** *adj.* doing something for a living

**prop′er•ty** *n.* something that is owned

**prov′ėrb** *n.* a short saying meant to show something that is true

**pub′lic baths′** *n. pl.* a building having pools for bathing and relaxing in

**Puer•to** (pwĕr′tō) **Rï′cō** *n.* an island in the Atlantic Ocean southeast of the United States

**pū′pil** *n.* the dark opening in the colored part of the eye

**pўr′a•mid** *n.* a solid shape that has a square bottom and four triangular sides

**quench** *v.* to satisfy [thirst]

**quick′ėn** *v.* to become faster

**quiv′er•ing** *adj.* trembling

**race** *n.* a large group of people who look alike in certain ways such as skin color

**raft** *n.* a large number

**raġe** *v.* to move wildly

**rānġe** *n.* a line of things such as mountains

**rap′id** *n.* a part of a river that runs very fast

**rate** *n.* the speed at which something is done

**re·call′** *v.* to remember

**re·flec′tion** *n.* the picture seen in a mirror or other shiny surface

**re·fresh′ment man** *n.* one who sells snacks in a public place

**re·gret′** *v.* to be sorry about

**re·joice′** *v.* to feel or show great gladness

**re·join′** *v.* to get back together with

**re·lief′** *n.* an end to worry

**rep·u·ta′tion** *n.* what others think of a person or thing

**re·serve′** *n.* land set aside for some use

**rē′sōurce** (*or* **re·sōrce′**) *n.* a useful thing

**re·spon′si·bil′i·ty** *n.* 1. being in charge 2. what a person must do; a duty

**ret′i·na** *n.* a lining at the back of the eye

**rhi·noc·er·os** (rī·noc′er·os) *n.* a large African animal that has one or two horns on its nose

**rich** *adj.* having what is needed to grow healthy plants

**Rí·o** (rī′ō) **Grän′de de Sän·tiä′gō** *n.* a large river in Mexico

**Rí·o Pie·dras** (rī′ō) (pyě′dräs) *n.* a town in Puerto Rico

**rō′dent** *n.* a type of animal that has large front teeth (Rats, rabbits, and squirrels are rodents.)

**roy′al** *adj.* belonging to a king or queen

**rub′ble** *n.* bits and pieces of broken stones

**Rus·sia** *n.* a large country in Europe and Asia

**Sa·här′a** *or* **Sa·här′a** *n.* the largest desert in the world

**Sän′chō**

**Sän Juan** (hwän) *n.* the capital city of Puerto Rico

**scav′en·ġer** *n.* an animal that eats meat it has not killed itself

**seal** *v.* to close up tight—*n.* a design stamped in clay or wax to show ownership

**sea′pōrt** *n.* a place for ocean ships to dock

**sea′sīde** *adj.* beside the ocean

**sea′son** *n.* one of the four parts of the year (spring, for example)

**sel′dom** *adv.* not often

**se•ñor** (sen•yōr′) *n.* the Spanish word for "mister" or "sir"

**se•ño•ri•ta** (sen•yô•rĭ′tä) *n.* the Spanish word for "miss" or "young woman"

**sense** *n.* a feeling

**ses′sion** *n.* a meeting for a certain purpose

**set sail′** to start a trip by sea

**shaft** *n.* 1. a ray or beam 2. a narrow opening

**shan't** *v.* a short form of "shall not"

**shiv′er** *v.* to shake with cold, fear, or excitement

**shrub** *n.* a bush

**shuf′fle** *v.* to drag the feet while walking

**Si•a•mese′** *adj.* from the old country of Siam, now called Thailand (tï′länd)

**sil•hou•ette** (sil•ōō•et′) *n.* a dark figure against a light background

**sim′i•lar** *adj.* like

**slack off** *v.* to slow down

**snake** *v.* to slide from side to side

**so′cial life′** *n.* time spent relaxing with others

**soil** *n.* dirt; earth

**so′lar** *adj.* having to do with the sun

**South′ Pole′** *n.* the most southern point of the earth

**Sō′vi•et Ūn′ïon** *n.* a huge area of land (made up of Russia and other countries)

**Spain** *n.* a country in southern Europe

**span** *n.* the width of something

**Span′ish** *n.* the language of Spain and most of South and Central America

**spell** *n.* a work of magic

**splin′ter** *v.* to break into very small parts

**sprawl** *v.* to sit or lie with arms and legs spread out

**stalk** (stak) *v.* to follow something in order to catch it; to hunt

**stand firm** to refuse to change one's mind

**stär′tle** *v.* to surprise

**state** *n.* a condition

**stop′ō•ver** *n.* a short rest during a trip

**stop short** *v.* to halt suddenly

**stōw′a•way′** *n.* a person who hides away (usually on a ship)

**struc′ture** *n.* something that has been built

**stub′by** *adj.* short and thick

**stud′y** *n.* a picture made to show what something looks like

**stunned** *adj.* shocked or surprised

**style** *n.* a way of painting that shows who the artist is

**sub'ject** *n.* something written about

**su·ki·ya·ki** (skï·yä'kï) *n.* a Japanese food

**Sung** *n.* one of the ancient kingdoms in what is now China

**sup·port'** *v.* to provide with necessary things such as food

**sup·press'** *v.* to hold back or hold down

**sur·pass'** *v.* to be better than

**sur·round'ings** *n. pl.* the things around a person, animal, or place

**sus·tained'** *adj.* continued for a certain length of time

**Swä·hï'lï** *n.* a language spoken mainly in eastern Africa

**sys'tem of** (ôv) **meas'ures** *n.* the way people of a certain place measure the size of objects (in yards or meters, for example)

**sys'tem of** (ôv) **mon'ey** *n.* the kind of money people of a certain place use (dollars or marks, for example)

**sys'tem of** (ôv) **weights** (wāts) *n.* the way people of a certain place weigh objects (in pounds or kilograms, for example)

**Pronunciation Key**

VOWELS: sat, hăve, āble, fäther, all, câre, álone; yet, brĕad, mē, loadèd; it, practĭce, pīlot, machïne; hot, nō, ôff, wagòn; foŏt, foōd; oil, toy; count, town; up, ūse, trŭth, pǔll; mўth, baby, crў, zephўr.

CONSONANTS: cent, cider, cycle; c̄horus, c̲hute; ġem; light and though (silent), ghost; iñk; elephant; toe̲s; them; special, mea̲sure, na̲tion, na̲ture.

**sys'tem of** (ôv) **writ'ing** *n.* the letters or symbols people of a certain place use (letters of the roman or cyrillic alphabet, for example)

**Tä·hï'tï** *n.* an island in the southern Pacific Ocean

**Tä Mä·te'te** *n.* Polynesian words for "the marketplace" or "the market"

**tame** *adj.* not wild

**Tär'shish** *n.* an ancient city mentioned in the Bible

**tax'ï** *v.* to roll down a runway before taking off

**tea' cärt** *n.* a small table on wheels

**tem'pèst** *n.* a storm

**tes'ta·mènt** *n.* a reminder

**there·af·ter** (th̲âr'af·ter) *adv.* after that time; from then on

**there·fore** (th̲âr'fore) *adv.* for that reason

**thrive** *v.* to grow or be healthy

**thun'der·òus** *adj.* making a loud, booming noise

**tick bird** *n.* a type of bird that eats insects living on a rhinoceros

**tō′fū** *n.* a kind of white, soft food made from soybeans

**toil** *n.* hard work

**Tō′ky•ō** *n.* the capital city of Japan

**tomb** (tūmb) *n.* a grave or building in which the dead are kept

**tō′tȧl** *adj.* complete

**trade** *v.* to buy and sell

**trȧ•di′tiȯn** *n.* a belief or a way of doing things that is followed for years

**trance** *n.* a state somewhat like sleep, in which a person does not think clearly

**trans•pâr′ėnt** *adj.* clear or easy to see through

**trop′i•cȧl** *adj.* 1. near the equator 2. hot and wet like the areas near the equator

**tun′drȧ** *n.* a treeless plain in a far northern area

**tū′nic** *n.* a long, loose shirt; a uniform jacket

**Tut•ankh•a•men** (tūt′änk•ä′mėn) *n.* the name of a king of Egypt

**twī′light** *n.* a time when it is not completely light or completely dark

**ug′li•ness** *n.* unpleasing appearance

**un•fȧ•mil′ïär** *adj.* hard to understand

**u•nique** (ū•nïk′) *adj.* unlike any other

**un•wïeld′y** *adj.* hard to manage

**ur′ġėn•cy** *n.* a need to do something right away

**ur′ġėnt** *adj.* needed right away

**ū•ten′sil** *n.* a tool

**van′ish** *v.* to disappear

**vâ′rïed** *adj.* different from one another

**vast** *adj.* huge

**vė•ran′dȧ** *n.* a porch

**Vė•sū′vi•us** *n.* an active volcano in Italy

**Vï•en′nȧ** *n.* the capital city of Austria

**vī′tȧl** *adj.* necessary or very important

**viv′id•ly** *adv.* in a way that makes something seem real

**vul′tȯre** *n.* a large bird that eats animals it did not kill itself

**walled gate** *n.* a gate in the walls surrounding an ancient city

**waltz** *n.* a kind of dance in which a couple spins in graceful circles

**wän′der** *v.* to travel aimlessly

**wâres** *n. pl.* the goods a merchant has to sell

**wā′ver•y** *adj.* shaking

**wêa′ry** *adj.* very tired

**Wei** (wā) *n.* one of the ancient kingdoms in what is now China

**Wel′ling•tòn boŏts** *n. pl.* high leather boots

**West′ern•er** *n.* a person from Europe or America

**Wey** (wā) **Wu̱** *n.* one of the ancient kingdoms in what is now China

**wīd′ėn** *v.* to become broader

**wĭld′life** *n.* animals that are not tame

**will′ing•ly** *adv.* without being forced

**wis′dòm** *n.* the ability to use knowledge; understanding

**witch** *n.* a woman who some say can do magic

**with•draw′** *v.* to back away

**Wō′lof** *n.* an African language

**wom′bat** *n.* an Australian animal that looks somewhat like a wild-cat and carries its babies in a pouch

**wòr′thy** *adj.* good enough to earn praise

**Yen** *n.* one of the ancient kingdoms in what is now China

**Yō•kō•hä′mä** *n.* a city in Japan

**Pronunciation Key**

VOWELS: sat, hăve, āble, fäther, a̱ll, câre, ȧlone; yet, brĕad, mē, loadėd; it, practĭce, pīlot, machīne; hot, nō, ôff, wagȯn; foŏt, f oōd; oil, toy; count, town; up, ūse, tru̱th, pu̱ll; mўth, baby, crȳ, zephȳr.

CONSONANTS: cent, cider, cycle; c̄horus, c̱hute; ġem; light and though (silent), ghost; iñk; elepḫant; toe s̱; ṯhem; spec̲ial, meas̲ure, nat̲ion, nat̲ure.

**Yô′ru̱•bȧ** *n.* the language spoken by certain people living in the western African coastal area

**Yu•eh** (yu̱•ĕ′) *n.* one of the ancient kingdoms in what is now China

**Zä•ïre′** *n.* a country in the center of Africa